Celebrate reading with us!

Cover and title page illustrations by Francisco X. Mora.

Acknowledgments appear on page 275.

1995 Impression

Printed in the U.S.A.

ISBN: 0-395-61086-9

456789-VH-96 95 94

Just Listen

Senior Author
John J. Pikulski

Senior Coordinating Author
J. David Cooper

Senior Consulting Author
William K. Durr

Coordinating Authors
Kathryn H. Au
M. Jean Greenlaw
Marjorie Y. Lipson
Susan E. Page
Sheila W. Valencia
Karen K. Wixson

Authors
Rosalinda B. Barrera
Edwina Bradley
Ruth P. Bunyan
Jacqueline L. Chaparro
Jacqueline C. Comas
Alan N. Crawford
Robert L. Hillerich
Timothy G. Johnson
Jana M. Mason
Pamela A. Mason
William E. Nagy
Joseph S. Renzulli
Alfredo Schifini

Senior Advisor
Richard C. Anderson

Advisors
Christopher J. Baker
Charles Peters
MaryEllen Vogt

HOUGHTON MIFFLIN COMPANY BOSTON
Atlanta Dallas Geneva, Illinois Palo Alto Princeton Toronto

FICTION

Award Winner

NONFICTION

THEME 3

REGION

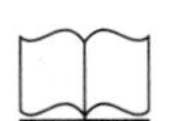

THEME BOOKS

I'm in Charge of Celebrations
by Byrd Baylor

Cactus Hotel
by Brenda Z. Guiberson

THEME 4

FANTASY

195

BEWARE! TROUBLE AHEAD

FICTION

THEME 1

FAMILY

Family Album

Pick up a family album and inside it you will find photographs of important times in the life of a family. Some of them are silly — a funny picture of a cousin jumping into the river with his clothes on. Some of them are special — a picture of a sister at her high school graduation. Each of the photographs tells a wonderful story.

In this *Family Album* you will read stories about three different families. Each story tells about an event that might become a memory in each family's Family Album.

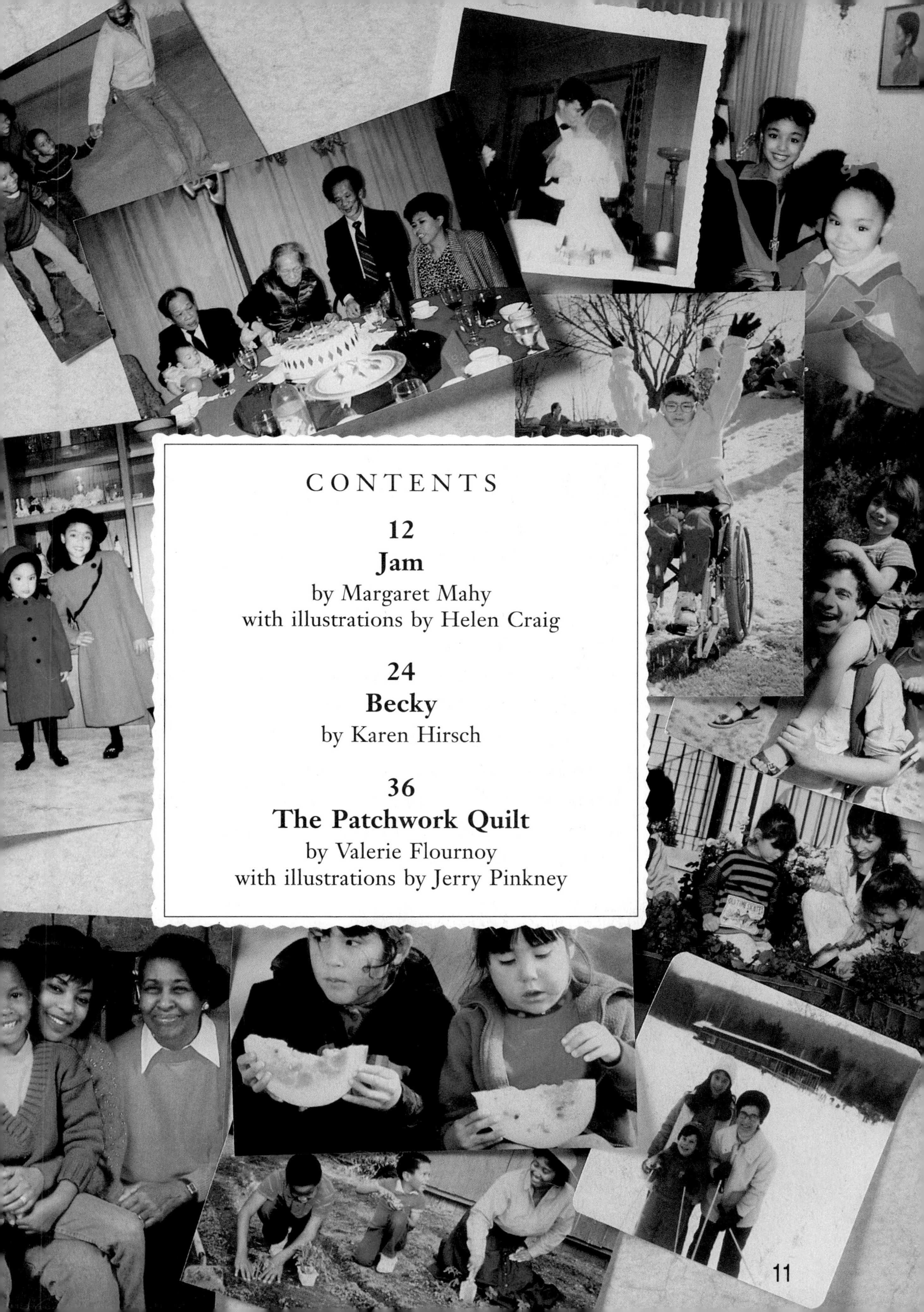

CONTENTS

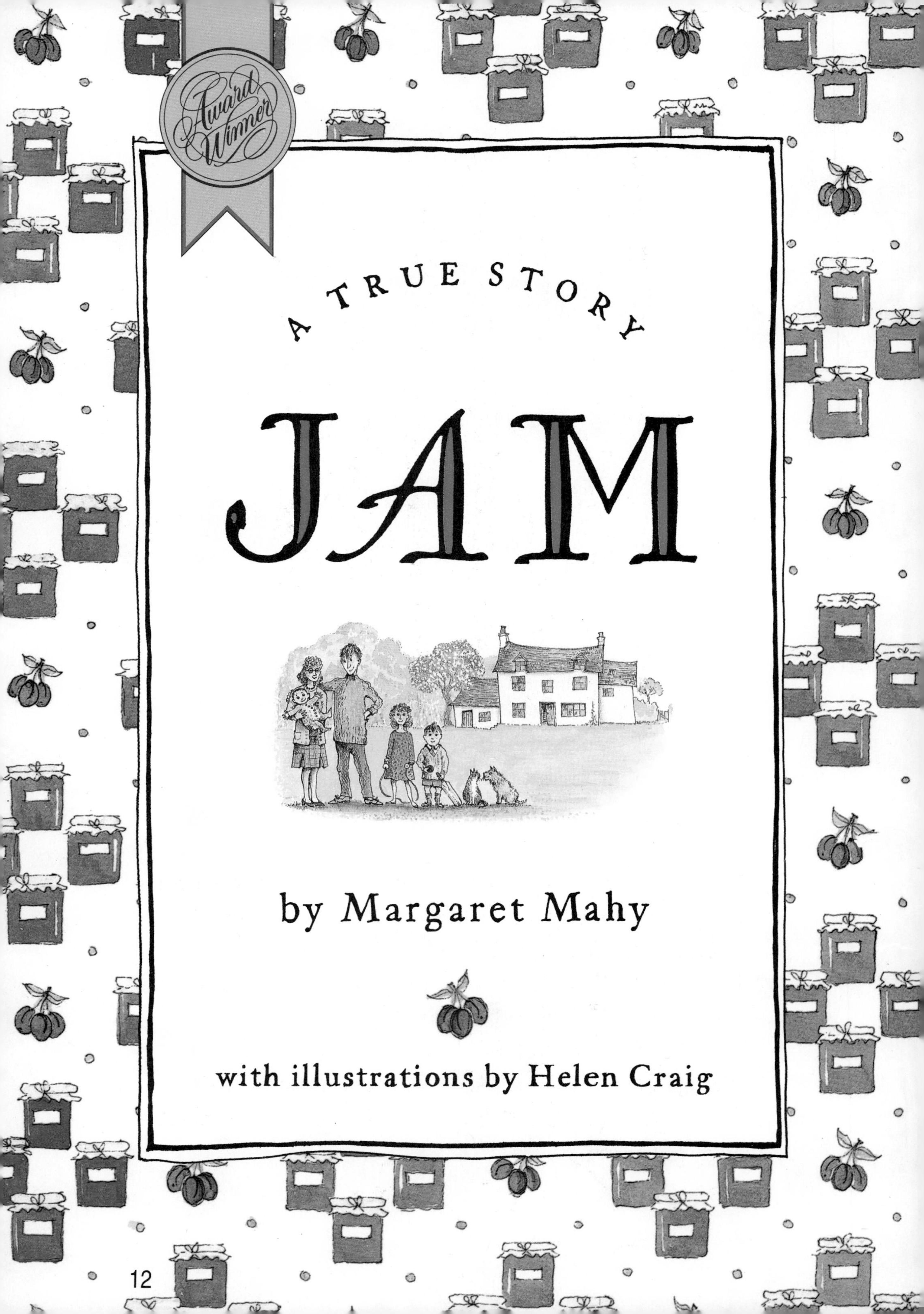

A TRUE STORY

JAM

by Margaret Mahy

with illustrations by Helen Craig

Mr. and Mrs. Castle lived in a white house with a big, green lawn. Their three children were called Clement, Clarissa, and Carlo.

"Three little Castles," said Mr. Castle, "but very small ones — more like Cottages, really."

Mrs. Castle was studying to be an atomic scientist.

"What a clever one *she* is," said Mr. Castle. "If she decided to go to the moon I don't think she'd even need a rocket to get there."

One day Mrs. Castle announced that she had found herself a job. Important scientists were developing an electronic medicine to cure sunspots, and they had sent for Mrs. Castle.

"But who is going to look after us?" asked Clement.

"Isn't anyone going to be here when we come home from school?" asked Clarissa. Carlo was too young to say anything, but he looked worried.

"*I* shall be here, my dear little Cottages," Mr. Castle cried. "You have no reason to be anxious."

He washed and dried the dishes. He vacuumed the carpets, put the dough to rise in a warm place, planted a row of cabbages, folded the wash, baked the bread *and* a cake . . .

He swept the house from top to bottom, wiped down the counter, had a quick cup of tea, put Carlo down for his afternoon sleep . . . had another cup of tea . . . prepared dinner . . .

cleaned the bath . . . read the paper . . . kissed the children when they came home from school — and Mrs. Castle when she came home from work — and asked them all what sort of day they had had.

Then he gave Mrs. Castle something to drink, handed her the paper, and took the children out for a game on the big, green lawn. He was an excellent housefather.

Indeed, he was so good that one day he actually ran out of work. While he tried to think of just what to do next, there came a soft thud on the roof, and then another one.

"Sunspots!" cried Mr. Castle, and ran outside. It was not the sound of falling sunspots he had heard, but ripe plums tumbling off the old plum tree that grew behind the house.

Mr. Castle was delighted. Gathering up the fallen plums he made three pots of plum jam.

"Jam! What a treat!" the children cried.

The next day many more plums fell from the tree and Mr. Castle made twenty pots of plum jam.

The following day the ground under the tree was covered with big, purple plums. That day Mr. Castle had enough plums to make thirty pots of jam.

But the day after that there were even more plums. Mr. Castle had run out of jam jars.

"What a challenge!" he cried. "Not a single plum must be wasted."

He filled all the vases in the house with jam. He filled all the glasses, too. Even Carlo's rabbit mug and the teapot were filled with jam.

"The whole house is like a jam factory," said Clement.

"It's like a school for jam pots," said Clarissa.

"Your father is a born artist," said Mrs. Castle. "He is the Picasso of jam makers."

"Now all the work is done," said Mr. Castle, looking pleased. "We can look forward to eating this delicious jam all year long."

They began with jam sandwiches. Mrs. Castle, Clement, and Clarissa had jam sandwiches in the lunches Mr. Castle prepared for them every morning. Carlo, who was cutting new teeth, had jam on his crusts.

"Hooray!" called Mr. Castle. "We've emptied the teapot already. We'll be able to have tea with our cakes, cookies, and tarts."

That winter the roof leaked a little. Mr. Castle's jam proved very useful, for as well as being delicious, it stopped leaks. When the tiles came off the bathroom floor, Mr. Castle stuck them down again with jam. After weeks of devoted jam eating they could put flowers in the vases again, and drink from glasses instead of from eggcups.

"I wouldn't really care if I never saw another pot of jam in my life," Clarissa whispered to Clement. "But don't tell Daddy I said so."

In the meantime they had jam with everything, and on everything, and under everything.

Their dreams became haunted with jam. Clement dreamed that the sky opened and jam rained down on him. Clarissa dreamed of fat, shadowy jam pots marching through the night, crying out a terrible war cry of "Jam! Jam! Jam!"

Mrs. Castle dreamed that it was proved that sunspots were caused by too much jam, and Carlo dreamed great jammy dreams as well. Their days were full of jam eating, and their nights of dreams all dripping with jam.

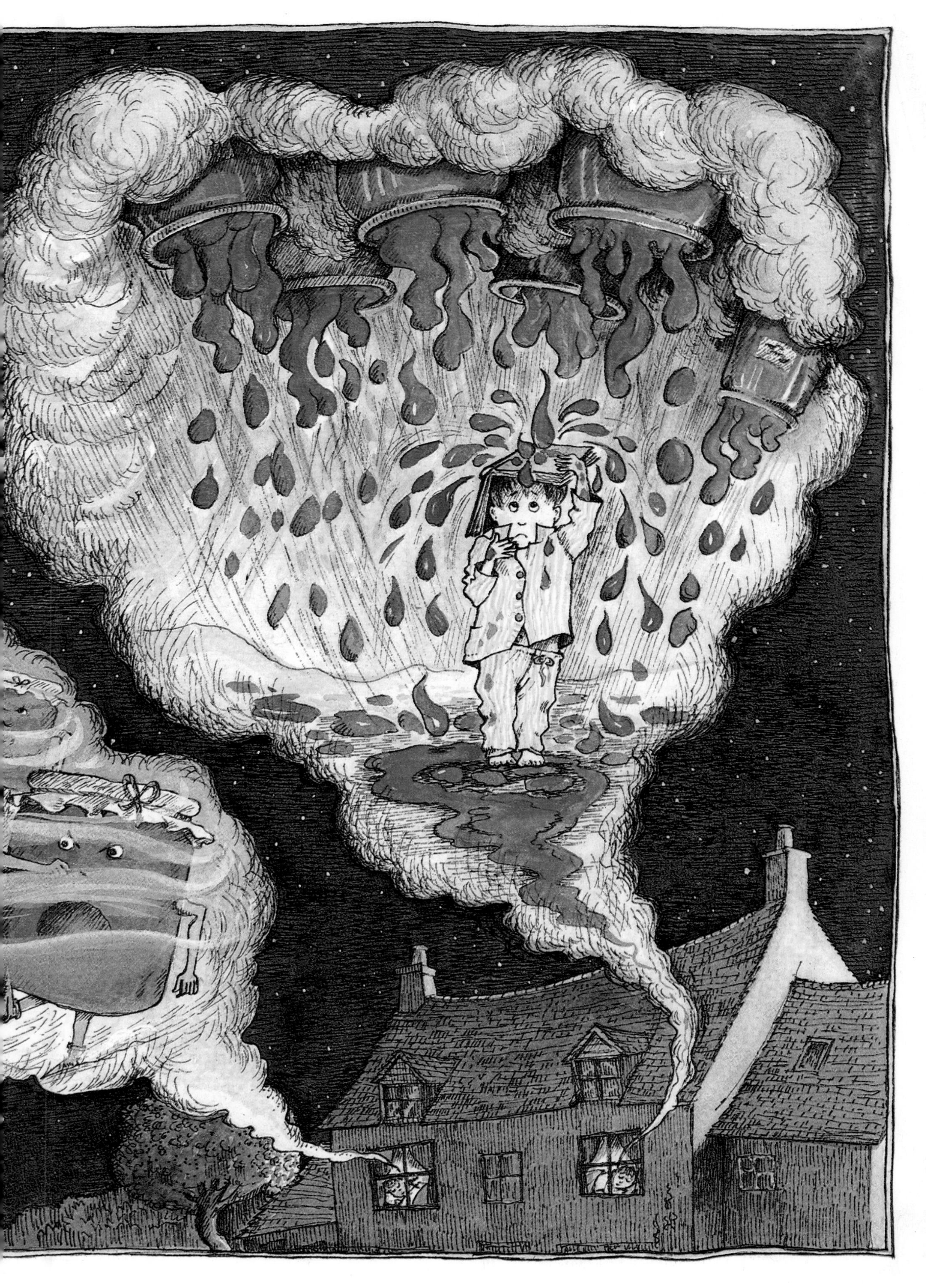

Finally, one morning Mr. Castle went to the cupboard to get down the next pot of jam only to find it was empty. There was not a single potful left.

"Let's have egg sandwiches for lunch," said Mrs. Castle.

"Spaghetti and salad," cried Clarissa.

"Let's have fish and chips," suggested Clement.

"But first let's have a game on the lawn," said Mr. Castle. "We've eaten so much jam that we look like jam pots ourselves. We shall have to get back in shape."

While they were playing on the lawn, Mr. Castle heard a soft thud on the roof.

The plums were ripe again.

101 USES FOR JAM

With a partner, list the ways the Castles might use up their next enormous batch of jam. Illustrate some of your suggestions. Make a booklet, and call it something like "101 Uses for Jam."

by Karen Hirsch ✦ illustrated by Renée Graef

Becky can't hear. When she was a baby she had a sickness that made her deaf. Even with her hearing aid, Becky can hear only big, loud noises. She can't hear our voices at all.

Becky is my part-time sister. She lives with our family from Monday until Friday so she can go to school. She has a real mom and dad and brothers and sisters, and she lives with them when it's not schooltime. They live on a farm.

It was a long time ago when I found out that Becky was coming to stay with us. I didn't like it.

"Why does she have to stay here, Mom?" I asked. "I don't want a kid here who I don't even know."

"I read a newspaper article about the hearing impaired program," my mom answered. "It said that homes were needed for the out-of-town children, and we have an extra room." She gave me a little hug. "Don't worry. You'll get to know her."

I wasn't so sure. That extra room had been my brother's and my playroom. Now they made it into a bedroom for Becky. Neither of us liked that. And how could I get to know her? She was deaf.

I was surprised when I first saw Becky. That was two years ago. I guess I thought she'd look different from other people. But there she was, in her jeans and tee-shirt and long ponytails, looking like anyone else.

It was in August, and she came with her parents to meet our family. She was scared at first. I was too. But after her mom and dad and my mom and dad had visited awhile, Becky and I started looking at each other. I couldn't believe that she was deaf. I walked across the room.

"Want to play?" I asked.

She didn't answer. She looked right at me and smiled a little. But she didn't say anything. I felt so strange. I didn't know what to do. So I just left the room.

Becky moved in the day before school opened. She came in a car with her mom and dad and five of her brothers and sisters. They all helped carry in Becky's things. I watched from the garage.

Becky didn't smile at all. Her big brother tickled her a couple of times, and her little sister gave her a licorice candy. They all hugged her and kissed her good-bye. But Becky just stood there, hardly moving.

I found a frisbee on the woodpile and took it outside. "Want to play?" I asked. I held the frisbee up so she'd understand.

We played frisbee for a while. Then I found my stilts and helped Becky walk on them. She got the hang of it right away. She went all the way down the driveway and back before she fell off.

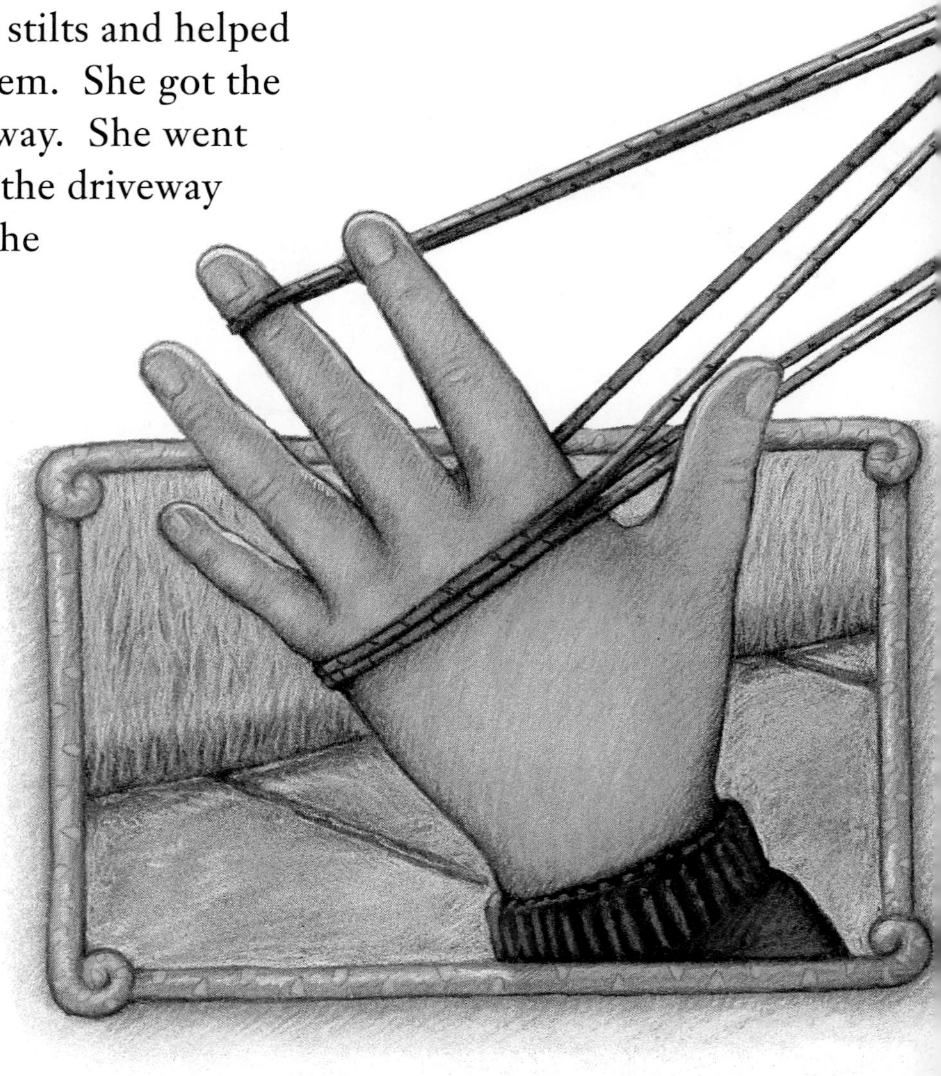

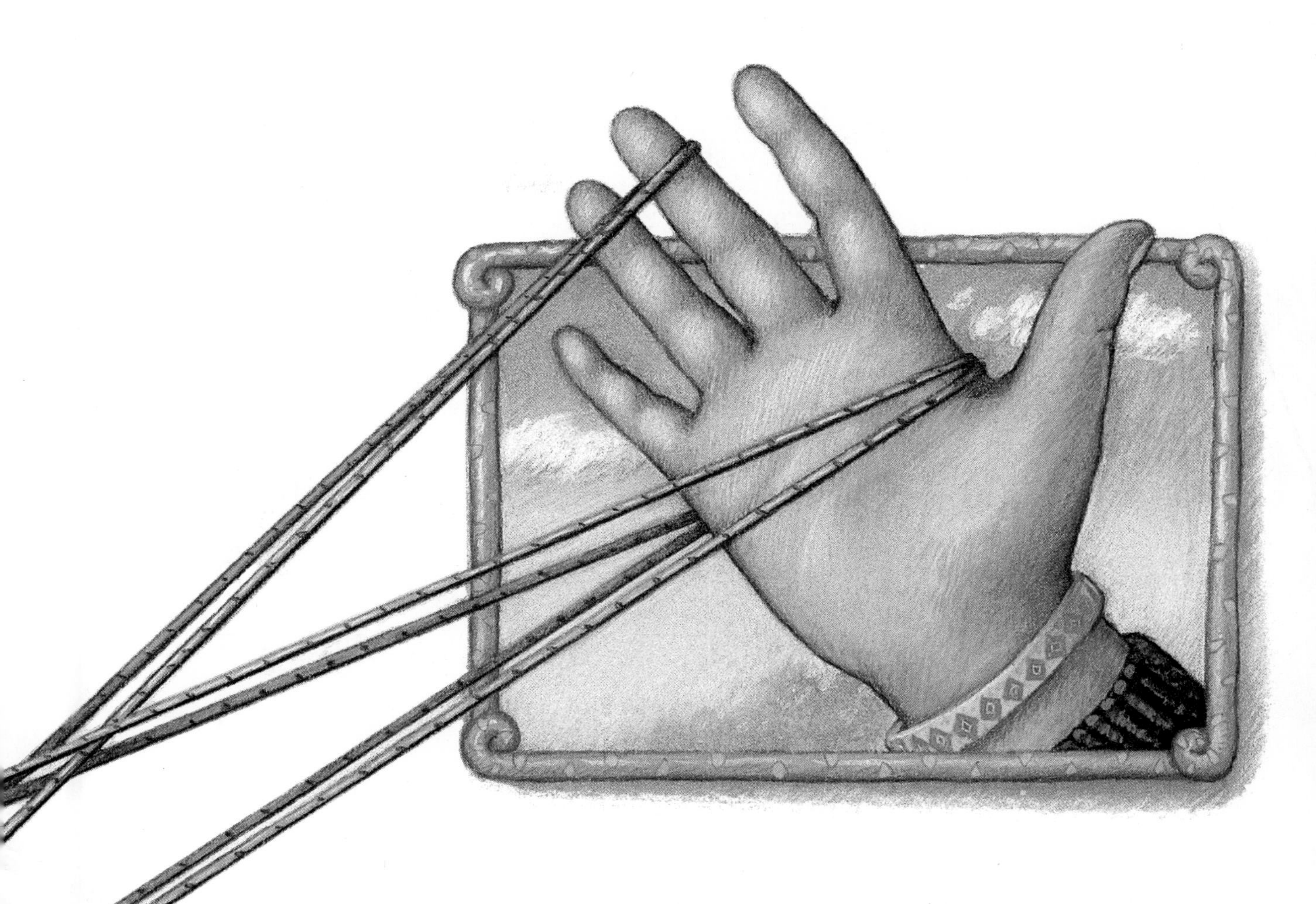

Then she looked right at me and smiled. She reached into her jacket pocket and pulled out a strong string tied into a long loop. She put the string around her hands and started flipping it every which way. She ended up with the string crossed and zigzagged in a pretty design. I'd never seen anything like it.

Then Becky took the string off and handed me the loop. She grinned and pointed at the string and at me. I wanted to try it, but I didn't know how. I shrugged my shoulders. Becky put the string on my hands and showed me what to do.

Most of the time it was really nice having Becky around. Especially on rainy days. Then we painted pictures or did gymnastics. Sometimes we made puppets or helped my dad make chocolate cake. We played the string game, too. Becky showed me a bunch of designs. Some we did together.

"It's called Cat's Cradle," my mom said when I told her about the game Becky had taught me. "It's an old, old game, and all of the designs have names."

The one thing we had trouble with was talking. Then Becky began to learn sign language in school. She learned to talk with her hands. She began to spell out words, letter by letter, and she also learned to sign whole words at a time. My mom and dad took a class to learn sign language and they taught me. That helped because then we could talk to Becky.

Becky also began learning to read lips. We looked right at her and talked in words and sign language at the same time.

Sometimes after school Becky played kickball and foursquare with me and my friends. It went okay usually, but sometimes I got mad at Becky.

When the rules to a game were hard and I couldn't explain them in signs, Becky cried and wanted to play anyway. My friends got mad then, too. "Get her out of the game," they said. "She's goofing it up."

"Go home to Mom," I signed to Becky.

"No!" she signed back. "I want to play!" She cried harder. I took her home then, or Mom heard the fight and came and got her.

Since Becky can't hear, she can't hear her own voice either. She makes loud noises sometimes. But she doesn't know she's doing it.

One day we were at the library — my dad, Becky, and I. Becky saw a man on crutches, and she was so curious she began to point and sign.

"The man is hurt?" she signed. Then she made loud squealing sounds. People all over the library stared. It didn't help to say "Shhh," because Becky didn't know she was making sounds.

My dad explained to the man, and we left. We talked about it in the car.

"There's more she wants to say," my dad said. "She feels upset that she doesn't know all the words she needs yet."

Another time Becky was angry because she couldn't make us understand something at a shopping center.

"I want to go see the — " she signed, and then she stopped. She didn't know the sign for the next word, or maybe she couldn't spell it. She cried and squealed.

"The pet shop?" my mom signed.

"NO!" Becky signed.

"The ice cream shop?" my mom asked in sign language.

"NO!" Becky signed. She cried again and wouldn't let my mom near her.

A man was watching. "Look at that bratty, spoiled kid," he said to his son. That made me mad.

"She is not bratty," I said. "She can't hear. That's all." The man's face got red and he hurried away.

Later these things didn't happen so often because Becky's signing got better and better. Besides, we got used to it too. It was just part of Becky.

One night my mom and I had an argument over my piano lessons. School had just started, so Becky was back with us. My horrible piano lessons were starting the next day. I tried and tried to tell my mom that I didn't want to play the piano. She wouldn't even discuss it, she said. I had to take lessons at least one more year. A half hour of practice a day, she said.

I didn't want to cry, but I got so mad that I couldn't help it. Then I felt someone touch my shoulder. It was Becky.

"Let's go upstairs," she signed. She put her arm over my shoulder. We went to her room and I cried awhile. It was nice to have Becky with me.

A little while after that Becky and I decided to change her bedroom back into a playroom and have my room be a bedroom for both of us. Then we had more fun together.

When we had pillow fights, Mom told us to stop it. It was funny to see her yelling at us in sign language!

Becky will be with us for only one more month. It'll be summer then and she'll go home. Next fall she'll be going to a boarding school for deaf children. I felt sad when I heard about that. Dad told me just last week when Becky and I were helping him wash the car.

"Why can't she stay here and keep going to this school?" I asked.

My dad handed Becky and me the bucket of soapy water and a rag. "Her parents believe that she'll get a better education there," he explained. "But don't worry. We'll always be friends with Becky."

"But Becky's almost my sister!" I said.

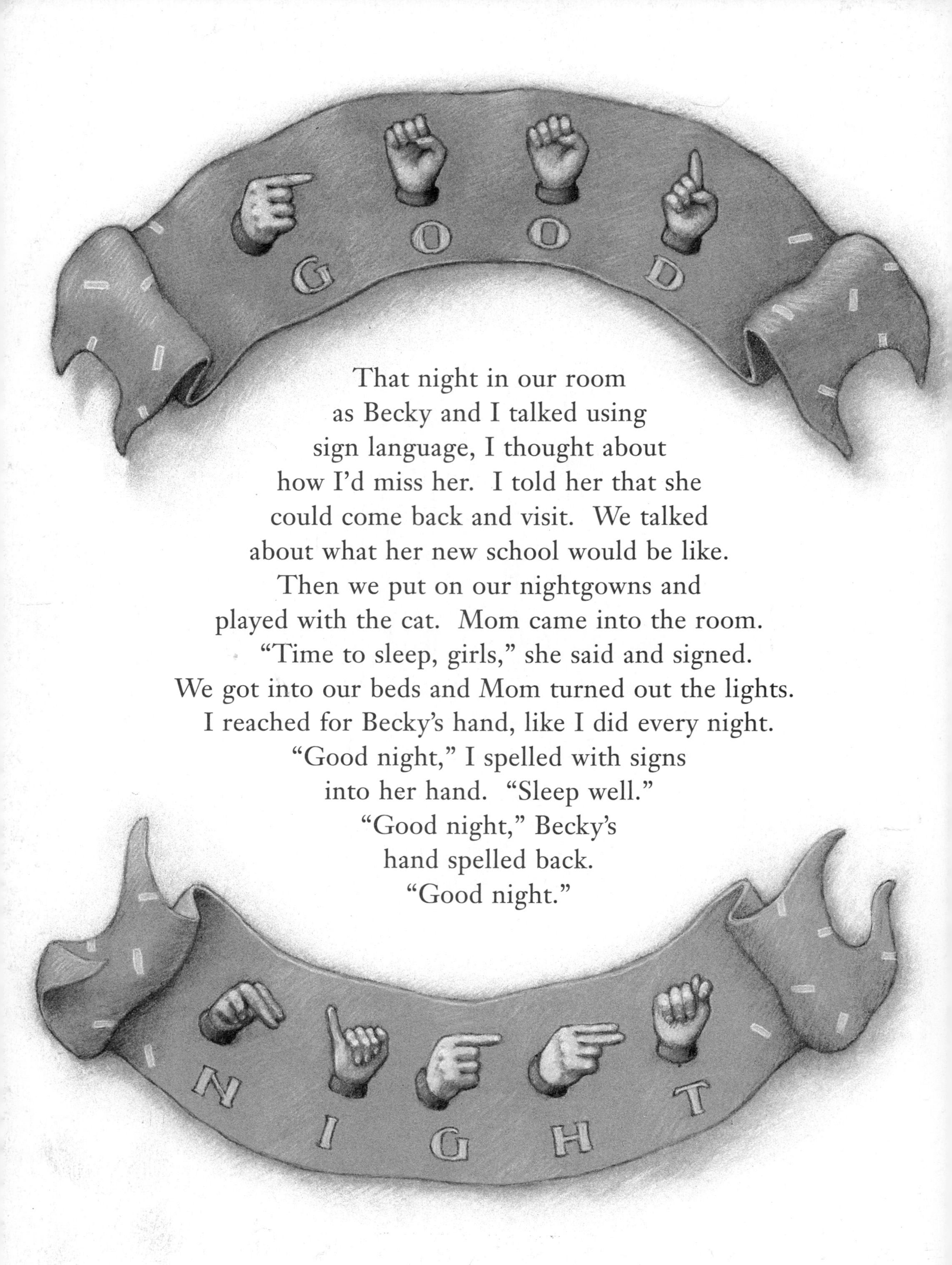

That night in our room
as Becky and I talked using
sign language, I thought about
how I'd miss her. I told her that she
could come back and visit. We talked
about what her new school would be like.
Then we put on our nightgowns and
played with the cat. Mom came into the room.
"Time to sleep, girls," she said and signed.
We got into our beds and Mom turned out the lights.
I reached for Becky's hand, like I did every night.
"Good night," I spelled with signs
into her hand. "Sleep well."
"Good night," Becky's
hand spelled back.
"Good night."

A SCRAPBOOK FOR BECKY

Make a scrapbook for Becky to take with her when she leaves to go to her new school. Think of things she might like to remember, like painting pictures, baking a chocolate cake, and having pillow fights. Then make drawings or cut out pictures from old magazines to make Becky's scrapbook. If you like, add a few words to go with your drawings and pictures.

Andre

I had a dream last night. I dreamed
I had to pick a Mother out.
I had to choose a Father too.
At first, I wondered what to do,
There were so many there, it seemed,
Short and tall and thin and stout.

But just before I sprang awake,
I knew what parents I would take.

And *this* surprised and made me glad:
They were the ones I always had!

Gwendolyn Brooks

Poetry Album

Everybody Says

Everybody says
I look just like my mother.
Everybody says
I'm the image of Aunt Bee.
Everybody says
My nose is like my father's,
But *I* want to look like *me*.

Dorothy Aldis

Mother's Day

Because it was Mother's Day
I gave a present to my mother.
Without saying anything
she looked at me
almost crying.
I hid my face with my skirt.

Takeuchi Yumiko, age 8

The Patchwork Quilt

Written by
Valerie Flournoy
◆
Illustrated by
Jerry Pinkney

Tanya sat restlessly on her chair by the kitchen window. For several days she had had to stay in bed with a cold. But now Tanya's cold was almost gone. She was anxious to go outside and enjoy the fresh air and the arrival of spring.

"Mama, when can I go outside?" asked Tanya. Mama pulled the tray of biscuits from the oven and placed it on the counter.

"In time," she murmured. "All in good time."

Tanya gazed through the window and saw her two brothers, Ted and Jim, and Papa building the new backyard fence.

"I'm gonna talk to Grandma," she said.

Grandma was sitting in her favorite spot — the big soft chair in front of the picture window. In her lap were scraps of materials of all textures and colors. Tanya recognized some of them. The plaid was from Papa's old work shirt, and the red scraps were from the shirt Ted had torn that winter.

"Whatcha gonna do with all that stuff?" Tanya asked.

"Stuff? These ain't stuff. These little pieces gonna make me a quilt, a patchwork quilt."

Tanya tilted her head. "I know what a quilt is, Grandma. There's one on your bed, but it's old and dirty and Mama can never get it clean."

Grandma sighed. "It ain't dirty, honey. It's worn, the way it's supposed to be."

Grandma flexed her fingers to keep them from stiffening. She sucked in some air and said, "My mother made me a quilt when I wasn't any older than you. But sometimes the old ways are forgotten."

Tanya leaned against the chair and rested her head on her grandmother's shoulder.

Just then Mama walked in with two glasses of milk and some biscuits. Mama looked at the scraps of material that were scattered all over. "Grandma," she said, "I just cleaned this room, and now it's a mess."

"It's not a mess, Mama," Tanya said through a mouthful of biscuit. "It's a quilt."

"A quilt! You don't need these scraps. I can get you a quilt," Mama said.

Grandma looked at her daughter and then turned to her grandchild. "Yes, your mama can get you a quilt from any department store. But it won't be like my patchwork quilt, and it won't last as long either."

Mama looked at Grandma, then picked up Tanya's empty glass and went to make lunch.

Grandma's eyes grew dark and distant. She turned away from Tanya and gazed out the window, absentmindedly rubbing the pieces of material through her fingers.

"Grandma, I'll help you make your quilt," Tanya said.

"Thank you, honey."

"Let's start right now. We'll be finished in no time."

Grandma held Tanya close and patted her head. "It's gonna take quite a while to make this quilt, not a couple of days or a week — not even a month. A good quilt, a masterpiece . . ." Grandma's eyes shone at the thought. "Why I need more material. More gold and blue, some red and green. And I'll need the time to do it right. It'll take me a year at least."

"A year," shouted Tanya. "That's too long. I can't wait that long, Grandma."

Grandma laughed. "A year ain't that long, honey. Makin' this quilt gonna be a joy. Now run along and let Grandma rest." Grandma turned her head toward the sunlight and closed her eyes.

"I'm gonna make a masterpiece," she murmured, clutching a scrap of cloth in her hand, just before she fell asleep.

"We'll have to get you a new pair and use these old ones for rags," Mama said as she hung the last piece of wash on the clothesline one August afternoon.

Jim was miserable. His favorite blue corduroy pants had been held together with patches; now they were beyond repair.

"Bring them here," Grandma said.

Grandma took part of the pant leg and cut a few blue squares. Jim gave her a hug and watched her add his patches to the others.

"A quilt won't forget. It can tell your life story," she said.

The arrival of autumn meant school and Halloween. This year Tanya would be an African princess. She danced around in the long, flowing robes Mama had made from several yards of colorful material. The old bracelets and earrings Tanya had found in a trunk in the attic jingled noisily as she moved. Grandma cut some squares out of the leftover scraps and added Tanya to the quilt too!

The days grew colder but Tanya and her brothers didn't mind. They knew snow wasn't far away. Mama dreaded winter's coming. Every year she would plead with Grandma to move away from the drafty window, but Grandma wouldn't budge.

"Grandma, please," Mama scolded. "You can sit here by the heater."

"I'm not your grandmother, I'm your mother," Grandma said. "And I'm gonna sit here in the Lord's light and make my masterpiece."

It was the end of November when Ted, Jim, and Tanya got their wish. They awoke one morning to find everything in sight covered with snow. Tanya got dressed and flew down the stairs. Ted and Jim, and even Mama and Papa, were already outside.

"I don't like leaving Grandma in that house by herself," Mama said. "I know she's lonely."

Tanya pulled herself out of the snow being careful not to ruin her angel. "Grandma isn't lonely," Tanya said happily. "She and the quilt are telling each other stories."

Mama glanced questioningly at Tanya, "Telling each other stories?"

"Yes, Grandma says a quilt never forgets!"

The family spent the morning and most of the afternoon sledding down the hill. Finally, when they were all numb from the cold, they went inside for hot chocolate and sandwiches.

"I think I'll go sit and talk to Grandma," Mama said.

"Then she can explain to you about our quilt — our very own family quilt," Tanya said.

Mama saw the mischievous glint in her youngest child's eyes.

"Why, I may just have her do that, young lady," Mama said as she walked out of the kitchen.

Tanya leaned over the table to see into the living room. Grandma was hunched over, her eyes close to the fabric as she made tiny stitches. Mama sat at the old woman's feet. Tanya couldn't hear what was said but she knew Grandma was telling Mama all about quilts and how *this* quilt would be very special. Tanya sipped her chocolate slowly, then she saw Mama pick up a piece of fabric, rub it with her fingers, and smile.

From that moment on both women spent their winter evenings working on the quilt. Mama did the sewing while Grandma cut the fabrics and placed the scraps in a pattern of colors. Even while they were cooking and baking all their Christmas specialties during the day, at

night they still worked on the quilt. Only once did Mama put it aside. She wanted to wear something special Christmas night, so she bought some gold material and made a beautiful dress. Tanya knew without asking that the gold scraps would be in the quilt too.

There was much singing and laughing that Christmas. All Grandma's sons and daughters and nieces and nephews came to pay their respects. The Christmas tree lights shone brightly, filling the room with sparkling colors. Later, when everyone had gone home, Papa said he had never felt so much happiness in the house. And Mama agreed.

When Tanya got downstairs the next morning, she found Papa fixing pancakes.

"Is today a special day too?" asked Jim.

"Where's Mama?" asked Tanya.

"Grandma doesn't feel well this morning," Papa said. "Your mother is with her now till the doctor gets here."

"Will Grandma be all right?" Ted asked.

Papa rubbed his son's head and smiled. "There's nothing for you to worry about. We'll take care of Grandma."

Tanya looked into the living room. There on the back of the big chair rested the patchwork quilt. It was folded neatly, just as Grandma had left it.

"Mother didn't want us to know she wasn't feeling well. She thought it would spoil our Christmas," Mama told them later, her face drawn and tired, her eyes a puffy red. "Now it's up to all of us to be quiet and make her as comfortable as possible." Papa put an arm around Mama's shoulder.

"Can we see Grandma?" Tanya asked.

"No, not tonight," Papa said. "Grandma needs plenty of rest."

It was nearly a week, the day before New Year's, before the children were permitted to see their grandmother. She looked tired and spoke in whispers.

"We miss you, Grandma," Ted said.

"And your muffins and hot chocolate," added Jim. Grandma smiled.

"Your quilt misses you too, Grandma," Tanya said. Grandma's smile faded from her lips. Her eyes grew cloudy.

"My masterpiece," Grandma sighed. "It would have been beautiful. Almost half finished." The old woman closed her eyes and turned away from her grandchildren. Papa whispered it was time to leave. Ted, Jim, and Tanya crept from the room.

Tanya walked slowly to where the quilt lay. She had seen Grandma and Mama work on it. Tanya thought real hard. She knew how to cut the scraps, but she wasn't certain of the rest. Just then Tanya felt a hand resting on her shoulder. She looked up and saw Mama.

"Tomorrow," Mama said.

New Year's Day was the beginning. After the dishes were washed and put away, Tanya and Mama examined the quilt.

"You cut more squares, Tanya, while I stitch some patches together," Mama said.

Tanya snipped and trimmed the scraps of material till her hands hurt from the scissors. Mama watched her carefully, making sure the squares were all the same size. The next day was the same as the last. More snipping and cutting. But Mama couldn't always be around to watch Tanya work. Grandma had to be looked after. So Tanya worked by herself. Then one night, as Papa read them stories, Jim walked over and looked at the quilt. In it he saw patches of blue. His blue. Without saying a word Jim picked up the scissors and some scraps and started to make squares. Ted helped Jim put the squares in piles while Mama showed Tanya how to join them.

Every day, as soon as she got home from school, Tanya worked on the quilt. Ted and Jim were too busy with sports, and Mama was looking after Grandma, so Tanya worked alone. But after a few weeks she stopped. Something was wrong — something was missing, Tanya thought. For days the quilt lay on the back of the chair. No one knew why Tanya had stopped working. Tanya would sit and look at the quilt. Finally she knew. Some*thing* wasn't missing. Some*one* was missing from the quilt.

That evening before she went to bed Tanya tiptoed into Grandma's room, a pair of scissors in her hand. She quietly lifted the end of Grandma's old quilt and carefully removed a few squares.

February and March came and went as Mama proudly watched her daughter work on the last few rows of patches. Tanya always found time for the quilt. Grandma had been watching too. The old woman had been getting stronger and stronger as the months passed. Once she was able, Papa would carry Grandma to her chair by the window. "I needs the Lord's light," Grandma said. Then she would sit and hum softly to herself and watch Tanya work.

"Yes, honey, this quilt is nothin' but a joy," Grandma said.

Summer vacation was almost here. One June day Tanya came home to find Grandma working on the quilt again! She had finished sewing the last few squares together; the stuffing was in place, and she was already pinning on the backing.

"Grandma!" Tanya shouted.

Grandma looked up. "Hush, child. It's almost time to do the quilting on these patches. But first I have some special finishing touches. . . ."

The next night Grandma cut the final thread with her teeth. "There. It's done," she said. Mama helped Grandma spread the quilt full length.

Nobody had realized how big it had gotten or how beautiful. Reds, greens, blues, and golds, light shades and dark, blended in and out throughout the quilt.

"It's beautiful," Papa said. He touched the gold patch, looked at Mama, and remembered. Jim remembered too. There was his blue and the red from Ted's shirt. There was Tanya's Halloween costume. And there was Grandma. Even though her patch was old, it fit right in.

They all remembered the past year. They especially remembered Tanya and all her work. So it had been decided. In the right hand corner of the last row of patches was delicately stitched, "For Tanya from your Mama and Grandma."

A Classroom Quilt

The patchwork quilt told the story of a year in the life of Tanya's family. Work with a group of classmates. Make a paper quilt that tells the story of some events that happened in your classroom.

First, fill a large sheet of paper with squares. Next, make patches by drawing or pasting a picture inside each square. When you are finished, hang the "quilt" in your classroom.

Author Album

These photographs are from the authors' own family albums. Can you tell which author is in each photo?

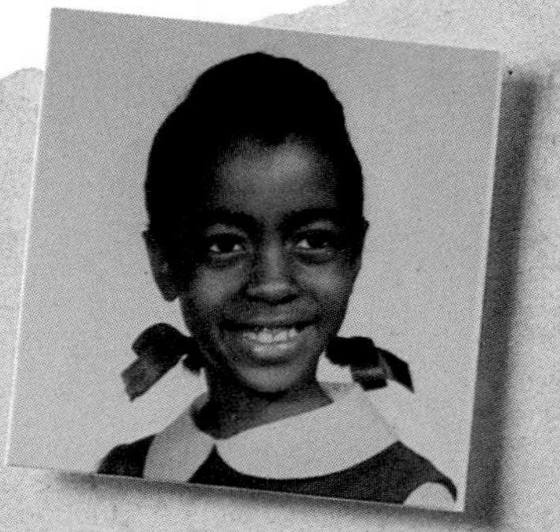

Margaret Mahy

Although Margaret Mahy's stories may seem a bit strange, she claims, "I always write about real life." "Real life" to Mahy may include a batch of jam that completely takes over a household, or as in *The Boy Who Was Followed Home,* a boy who is followed home by a hippopotamus.

Another Margaret Mahy book you might like is *The Man Whose Mother Was a Pirate,* about a man who takes his mother — who once was a pirate — to see the sea one last time.

Karen Hirsch

The character of Becky is based on a real little girl that Karen Hirsch knew. Some of the experiences Becky has, such as the scenes in the library and in the mall, are experiences that that little girl had. Is the story a true story then? No, it's fiction. Karen Hirsch says, "It makes for the best kind of writing if you write about something you know about." To create her stories she combines real experiences with characters and events that she makes up.

As she writes, she also tries to think about what children like and care about — the things she hears them talking about in the classrooms in which she teaches.

Valerie Flournoy

Just as the patchwork quilt recorded the happy memories of Tanya's family, Valerie Flournoy's stories record memories of her own life. "All the books I write are somewhat autobiographical," says the author. They reflect events that happened either to Flournoy herself, to a family member, or to a friend.

The Patchwork Quilt, which the author dedicated to her mother and grandmother, grew out of her interest in her own family history and her sadness that she hadn't gotten to know her grandmother better.

MORE

FAMILY ALBUMS

TO FLIP THROUGH

The Lost Lake
by Allen Say
Dad and Luke are off on an adventure to Lost Lake, a "special secret place" Dad once shared with his father. But are there any secret places left in the world? Go searching with Luke and his dad, and find out.

Grandmother's Christmas Story
by Richard Red Hawk
Grandmother tells about being lost as a child in the desert. A white man she called "Yellow Hair" rescued and cared for her. Years later, she comes to his rescue in this Native American Christmas story.

Tar Beach
by Faith Ringgold
On summer nights, Cassie Louise Lightfoot lies out on the rooftop of her family's apartment in Harlem. There she dreams of flying to wherever she wants for the rest of her life.

Julian, Dream Doctor *by Ann Cameron*
Julian is having a tough time figuring out a present to get for his dad's birthday. He does find out what Dad wants, but is he brave enough to get it?

Margaret Ziegler Is Horse-Crazy
by Crescent Dragonwagon
When Margaret Ziegler goes to Country Life Riding Day Camp, she thinks she will be the star rider. But only the comfort of her family can help her recover from her first day at camp.

Tonight Is Carnaval
by Arthur Dorros
There's much work to do before Carnaval in this town in Peru. While a boy and his family prepare for the big day, he thinks of how the whole festival will sing and dance to the music of his band.

NONFICTION

THEME 2

IT'S MAGIC

Ladies and gentlemen, girls and boys!
Who is the greatest magician who ever lived?
How does a princess *float* in midair?
How can *you* make a card disappear?
The answers are all inside this book. You will learn the secrets of the great magicians. You will discover the fun of becoming a magician yourself. You will be amazed by the incredible world of
It's Magic.

IT'S MAGIC

Contents

Illustrated by Leslie Holt Morrill

One day Ehrich Weiss would be called Houdini the Great. Now at nine he was already called the Prince of the Air. He swung through the air on a makeshift trapeze rigged to a tree. He wore long red stockings to make him look like a real circus aerialist.

His first performance was in an empty lot which Ehrich, his friends, and his younger brother, Theo, had turned into a circus. Admission was five cents. The boys did not make much money, but Ehrich's daring stunts made the audience applaud. He hung by his feet from the trapeze and picked up things with his teeth. They applauded louder! Ehrich loved the applause. It made him feel special.

Ehrich lived in Milwaukee, Wisconsin. He had been born in Budapest, Hungary, on March 24, 1874, but his parents had moved to the United States when he was a little boy. The five-cent circus was only one of the many things he and his brother did to earn money for his family, who were poor. He worked as a bootblack shining shoes. He sold newspapers on a street corner. Once he and Theo gathered and sold flowers.

A touring magician came to Milwaukee when Ehrich was twelve. His father took the boys to see the man. Ehrich watched the exciting wizard known as Dr. Lynn with amazement. For weeks he tried to figure out the secrets of the magician's tricks. He imagined what it would be like to be a real magician on a stage amazing people.

After seeing Dr. Lynn, Ehrich thought about magic tricks all the time. One snowy December day his family had no money for fuel. Inside the house it was almost as cold as it was outside. Ehrich desperately wanted to do something. Finally, he had an idea.

After work as a delivery boy he stood on the street in the shivery cold with a card pinned to his hat. The snow covered him like a snowman, but everyone could read the card. On it he had printed

CHRISTMAS IS COMING, TURKEYS ARE FAT
PLEASE DROP A QUARTER
IN THE MESSENGER BOY'S HAT.

He had to stand in the falling snow for only an hour. People walking by couldn't help laughing at the funny sight, and being pleased, they all dropped quarters in his hat. Then he raced home through the freezing cold. He stood at the front door and prepared his "trick." When his mother came to the door, he said, "Shake me, I'm magic."

His mother thought Ehrich was being foolish, but she did as he asked. A shower of silver coins dropped from Ehrich's hair, from behind his ears, and from under his coat sleeves. They even came out of his pant legs and the holes in his gloves. His mother had to laugh.

The library near Ehrich's house became his favorite place. He read all the books it had on magic and all the stories about the lives of famous magicians.

After a time he realized there were two things he wanted to do. He wanted to help his family, and he wanted to be a magician. If he became a good magician, he could earn enough money to help.

During the next few years Ehrich worked in a factory in New York cutting neckties, but all he thought about was magic. He would go without lunch to try out his tricks on the other workers.

One book he read over and over again was about a French magician named Jean Eugène Robert-Houdin. He had performed before the French emperor and for Queen Victoria of England. He became Ehrich's hero, and Ehrich dreamed of performing before the queen, too.

Another book he liked was written by Harry Kellar, a famous American magician. Ehrich admired his escape tricks most of all. He would try them out on his brother, Theo, tying Theo up and freeing him in almost no time at all. Ehrich had learned special ways of tying knots which made this possible.

At seventeen, Ehrich decided to quit his job. He would try to find work as a magician, and for this he wanted an exciting new name. He thought about the names of the famous magicians he had read about. Harry Kellar and Robert-Houdin, he said over and over to himself. Finally, he took Harry Kellar's first name and called himself Harry. Then he added an I to Robert-Houdin's last name. He was now HARRY HOUDINI. Harry and his friend Jacob Hyman formed an act and called themselves the Brothers Houdini.

Later Theo replaced Jacob in the act, and Harry and Theo performed wherever they could. Often this was in cafés or at parties and meetings. Sometimes it was onstage at a proper theater with other acts. Once they were hired to appear at the Imperial Music Hall. Harry put Theo into a sack. He put the sack inside a wooden box. Then he locked and tied up the box. Theo had to escape before the audience's eyes. It was a trick the two brothers had rehearsed successfully many times.

Harry called out, "When I clap my hands three times — behold a miracle!"

But this time Theo did not appear.

Harry repeated the command.

No Theo.

The orchestra played louder. The manager brought down the curtain. Harry quickly untied the box. Poor Theo was red and puffing. He had made his way out of the sack through a secret opening. But he had left the key that opened the box from the inside in their dressing room. Harry decided from then on to change places with Theo.

One day he was riding a streetcar to a performance. He carried all his magic equipment with him. He had ropes that looked as if they were one piece but could easily become two. He had cards that stuck to one another. He had a magic wand that sprouted flowers and scarves. And he also had a bottle of clear liquid that turned to red liquid when it was exposed to the air. The streetcar ride was a bumpy one. Harry had a difficult time holding onto the strap and to his box. Then — crash! went the box. Everything spilled onto the floor. The bottled liquid that turned red broke. A pretty girl was standing next to him. The girl's name was Bess. They became friends, and this was the girl Harry later married.

Harry and Bess traveled all over the country. She had always been interested in the stage herself and so became his assistant. But Harry did all the tricks. He liked the escape tricks best. Harry studied everything there was to know about locks — how they worked, the different kinds of locks, and how to open them. He discovered that by using a piece of crooked metal, called a pick, he could unlock locks without a key. Once he understood everything there was to know about locks and how they worked, he developed the skill to open a lock or handcuff in minutes without a key. He added new escape tricks with both locks and handcuffs into his act, often staying in the theater after the show was over to work out new tricks.

He would free himself from five pairs of handcuffs and a set of leg irons. He escaped from ten pairs of handcuffs and a strapped and padlocked straitjacket which held his arms tightly to the body so he could not move. Wherever he appeared a big sign read:

HARRY HOUDINI
The King of Handcuffs
The Monarch of Leg Shackles

But Harry wanted to be the greatest escape artist of all times. He had his legs locked in irons. Then he had himself locked into a real prison cell. In less than eight minutes he stood on the outside of his cell free from all the things that bound him. A new sign was made. It read:

HARRY HOUDINI
The King of Handcuffs
The Monarch of Leg Shackles
and
The Undisputed Champion
Jail Breaker!

Audiences loved Harry Houdini. He remembered his hero Robert-Houdin who performed his magic before Queen Victoria. He too wanted to perform before the queen. He went to England, but the elderly queen died before Harry could perform for her. Harry was disappointed.

He traveled to Germany and Italy and France, performing his escape tricks. He became even more famous than Robert-Houdin. Soon everyone was calling him the Great Houdini. After five years of traveling all over the Continent, he and Bess returned to the United States.

Harry discovered that it was not easy being famous. There were some people who said he was not really great. These people challenged him publicly. They would walk right up on the stage when he was performing and say he really hadn't locked the cuffs on his wrists or that the rope was a trick rope. But Harry had now perfected his tricks.

He let these challengers lock his cuffs and tie the ropes themselves. Then he still escaped.

There were also people who tried to imitate his act. Harry was angry about this. He had his own challenge printed in the newspaper. He offered anyone who accepted his challenge a lot of money.

I, HARRY HOUDINI,

DO HEREBY CHALLENGE
ANY PERSON IN THE WORLD
TO DUPLICATE MY RELEASE FROM
CUFFS, IRONS
AND STRAITJACKETS
UNDER TEST CONDITIONS.
THAT IS TO ENTIRELY STRIP,
BE THOROUGHLY SEARCHED,
MOUTH SEWED AND SEALED UP,
MAKING IT IMPOSSIBLE
TO CONCEAL KEYS,
SPRINGS OR LOCK PICKERS,
AND IN THAT STATE ESCAPE....

No one accepted his challenge.

Harry decided he would have to do tricks that were impossible for anyone else to do. He would add his gymnastic and athletic abilities to his act. He was a good swimmer and could stay underwater a long time.

He had a tremendous milk can brought onstage. It was bigger than he was. The can was filled with water. Then his wrists were handcuffed. He was placed inside the can. The water was over his head. His assistant put the top on the can and secured it with six locked padlocks. The audience was told to hold its breath for as long as it could. No one was able to do it for more than thirty seconds, and there was Harry still locked in the can covered with water! The audience was terrified. Some shouted for someone to get an ax and get Harry out. Almost three minutes went by before Harry, smiling and dripping wet, emerged from the can! Never had he received so much applause.

But Harry had to make the trick better.

Not long after he did the same trick again. This time he had the can he was locked in lowered into the river. Still, he got out.

But there were many other kinds of tricks Harry liked to perform. He had seen other magicians perform "vanishing" acts in which they made rabbits and birds disappear. The Great Houdini advertised that he was going to make an elephant vanish. The elephant's name was Jennie. She weighed ten thousand pounds and wore a bright-blue ribbon around her neck. Houdini with fifteen assistants led Jennie into a huge box and closed the door. A few moments later the Great Houdini opened the door to the box. The elephant had "disappeared."

But of all the acts he performed, Harry still liked the escape acts best. These took a great deal of training. Whenever he did a new act, he would train three or four weeks for it. He learned how to hold his breath for long periods of time. He practiced breathing in such a manner that he didn't need air for nearly two hours. He developed his muscles. He could be hit in the stomach without injury. His arms were powerful and able to hold tremendous weights. During one show he slipped and fractured a bone in his ankle. Harry stopped long enough to let a doctor look at it. But he was so strong he went right on with the act.

One day a young man challenged Harry's strength. He wanted to see if Harry could be hit in the stomach without feeling pain. Without warning the young man punched Harry in the stomach before he had time to tighten his incredibly strong stomach muscles. During that night's performance Harry was in a lot of pain, but he refused to tell Bess. They had an engagement in Detroit the following night, and Harry was not going to miss it.

"I won't disappoint my audience," Harry said when a doctor was finally called.

The doctor said he had appendicitis and had to go to the hospital, but this didn't stop Harry. The Great Houdini had a show to do.

The Garrick Theater in Detroit was filled to the last seat. The orchestra played a rousing chorus of "Pomp and Circumstance." The Great Houdini walked onto the stage. He made silver coins vanish in the air. He made them reappear clinking in a swinging crystal box. He made a pretty girl disappear and a blooming rose bush

take her place. He did card tricks, taking cards, it seemed, from the air. He did a trick called the Whirlwind of Colors, pulling hundreds of yards of silk streamers dry from a liquid-filled glass bowl and turning them into flags.

But he was beginning to feel very ill. Although his temperature was 104 degrees, he was determined to finish his act.

And so he did, but when it was over, he collapsed. A few days later he died. The Great Houdini had given his last show. That was in 1926.

So great was Houdini that he is still thought of as the greatest magician and escape artist who ever lived. His name means superstrength.

He was a magician extraordinary. He was the one, the only, the Great Houdini.

THE GREATEST WHO EVER LIVED?

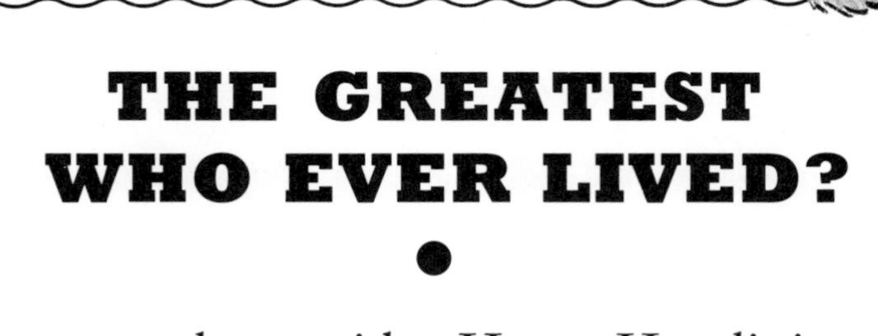

Many people consider Harry Houdini to be the greatest magician who ever lived. Now that you have read about Houdini, do you agree? Think about this question and how you would answer it.

Then write a short paragraph telling whether you agree or disagree.

Be sure to explain your answer.

TONIGHT
8 PM
HARRY KELLAR
SEE THE MARVEL
OF THE

The Floating Princess

from *Magicians Do Amazing Things* by Robert Kraske

Illustrations by Kevin Hawkes

The poster outside the theater read:

TONIGHT — 8pm
HARRY KELLAR
See the Marvel
of the
Floating Princess

On the poster was a drawing of Kellar. A man and a woman stood looking at it.

"Kellar has a bald head," said the man. "Just like my uncle."

The woman said, "He does not LOOK like a magician. I don't think he could fool anyone."

That is what many people said about Harry Kellar. But Kellar was one of the best magicians of the early 1900's. Another magician once said, "On the stage, Kellar does miracles!"

"The Floating Princess" was one of his very special "miracles."

People in the theater saw a young woman on the stage. She was lying on a sofa. She wore the costume of a princess from India. Her name was Princess Karnac.

". . . nine . . . eight . . . seven . . . six . . . " Kellar slowly counted as he hypnotized the princess. "You are falling into a deep sleep. Five . . . four . . . three . . . two . . . one. . . . Now you are sleeping . . . sleeping . . . a deep . . . deep . . . sleep. . . . "

Kellar turned to the people.

"Ladies and gentlemen. For hundreds of years, magicians in India have made people float in mid-air. After years of travel and study, I, Harry Kellar, have discovered the great secret. Watch!"

Kellar stepped over to the woman on the sofa. He waved his hands above her.

"Up!" he commanded.

For a moment, nothing happened. Princess Karnac stayed on the sofa. Then slowly she began to rise . . . up . . . up. Soon she was six feet in the air.

Kellar pulled away the sofa. There was nothing under the princess.

"Impossible!" people said. "She is floating in mid-air!"

A helper gave Kellar a large hoop about five feet wide. Kellar showed it to people in the first row.

"Please feel the hoop," he said. "Is it one piece? Make sure there are no spaces in it."

The people felt it. They looked at it closely. "Yes," they said. "The hoop is all in one piece."

"Then watch!" Kellar said.

Kellar went to the floating princess.

He placed the hoop over her head. Slowly he walked to her feet. The hoop passed along the woman's body. Then he walked the hoop back to her head.

Kellar then placed the hoop over the woman's feet. He walked it up to her head. The people saw the hoop pass again along her body. NOTHING WAS HOLDING HER UP!

Kellar gave the hoop to his helper. He pulled the sofa back under the princess.

He held up his hands. Slowly he lowered them. Gently, the woman floated down . . . down. . . . Then she rested on the sofa. Kellar clapped his hands once . . . twice . . . three times. The princess blinked. She sat up.

Kellar turned to the people and bowed. They clapped and cheered. They were amazed at what they had seen. A woman floating in mid-air!

Did Kellar perform a miracle? Did he really make the princess float in mid-air? What is your guess?

How Kellar Did It

Did you say that "The Floating Princess" was a clever trick? You were right. Onstage beside Kellar, you would have seen how the trick worked.

The woman was really lying on a board on the sofa. Her hair and dress covered it. A black iron bar went from the board through an opening in the curtain. The audience could not see the bar.

A helper stood behind the curtain. When Kellar said "Up!" the helper pulled a rope. The rope went over a wheel above the helper's head. Then it went down to the bar. The helper's pull lifted the bar, the board, and the princess. It looked as if she were floating in the air.

How could the hoop go along the woman's body?

The iron bar was bent in a long S curve. When Kellar moved the hoop from the woman's head to her feet, the hoop went into one curve of the S.

When he came to her feet, Kellar stopped. He could not move the hoop farther. Next he moved the hoop back to her head. He took it off and walked to her feet. There he placed the hoop around her feet and walked it to her head. The hoop went into the other curve of the S.

The audience thought the hoop passed all along the princess. But it didn't.

Was Princess Karnac a real princess? No. She was one of Kellar's helpers. Was she hypnotized? Not at all. She enjoyed a little rest.

With "The Floating Princess," the old "uncle" who didn't look like a magician fooled everyone. Did he fool YOU?

Write a speech introducing Harry Kellar's magic show.
Make the show seem exciting and mysterious.
Once you have written the speech, practice saying it.
Then present it to your class
as if they were actually going to see
the great Harry Kellar himself.

LADIES & GENTLEMEN
STEP RIGHT UP
see the
MYSTERIOUS
FLOATING
PRINCESS!

Before You Turn the Page

Most of the tricks you are about to read take no time at all to learn. It is still a good idea to practice them by yourself before doing them for an audience. This will give you confidence.

♥

Confidence Is a Magician's Best Friend.

If you mess up a trick, don't feel discouraged. Laugh about it or make a joke. Say something like this: "Some day I'll get this trick right. When I do, it won't be a trick. It will be a **miracle.**"

Six Magic Tricks You Can Do

1

2

3

4

5

6

from the book

Now You See It: Easy Magic for Beginners

by Ray Broekel and Laurence B. White, Jr.

The Balancing Straw

You'll need a plastic straw for this trick.

Place one end on your fingertip. The straw balances! It seems impossible. Everyone knows a straw balances only at its middle. But you balance it from one end.

Now hand the straw to a friend. When your friend tries to balance it, the straw falls. No one but you can do it.

How Is It Done?

Find a nail without a head. Slip it into one end of a straw. This makes that end heavy. The heavy end balances on your finger.

Tip the straw before you hand it to a friend. Secretly slip the nail out into your hand. Now the trick won't work. Your friend doesn't know about the secret nail! (Drop it into your pocket when nobody is watching.)

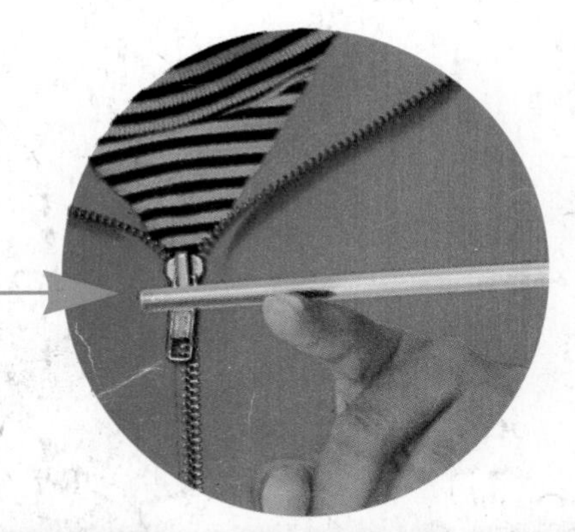

Fun with Your Thumb

You toss a handkerchief over your hand. Your thumb pokes up underneath. A friend takes hold of your thumb through the cloth. "Hold tight," you say. Then you walk away. Your friend is left holding your thumb!

How Is It Done?

This trick will be a big surprise. Nobody expects you to walk away leaving your thumb behind you.

You will need a raw carrot for the trick. Cut a piece off just about the size and shape of your thumb. Hide this in your hand.

Cover your hand with a handkerchief. Poke up the carrot. It will look like your thumb.

Ask someone to hold "your thumb" tightly. When that person does, take your hand away, hiding your thumb in your fist. Then you walk away as the person holds on to the carrot!

The Balancing Card

Give your friend one playing card. Ask him to balance it on the table. Tell him it must balance *on one edge.*

He tries, but the card falls. It falls every time he tries. Finally he will give up. Now you take the card. Presto! You do it the very first time.

How Is It Done?

You use a little trick. That's what a magician must do once in a while. Just before you set the card down you fix it in a certain way.

Here's how. Bend the card a little in the middle. The bend makes it balance easily!

4 Your Card Will Disappear

Ask a person to pick a card and remember it. Then place it back onto the deck, face down. You shuffle and mix the deck. "What was your card?" you ask.

The person names it. You say, "I will make that card disappear."

The cards are spread face up on the table. The card the person picked cannot be found. You have made it vanish!

How Is It Done?

Soap! Soap is your secret helper. Put a little dab of bar soap on the back of the top card in the deck. Have your friend choose a card from the middle. You have him put his card on top of the deck. Right on top of the soap card.

Make sure the two cards line up exactly. Now squeeze the deck. This makes the picked card stick to the soaped card.

Mix the deck and spread it face up on the table. The picked card will not be found. It is secretly stuck to the back of the soaped card.

The Rising Cards

You show a deck of cards and a paper cup. You place the cards in the cup, and hold the cup on your hand. You say, "Rise, card." A card slowly rises out of the deck. You say, "Rise, card," again. Another card mysteriously rises!

How Is It Done?

Find a paper cup that just holds a deck of cards. It must be a *paper* cup. Why? Because you must cut a hole in the bottom.

As you hold the cup, poke your middle finger up inside. Make sure nobody sees this finger. It is your finger that makes the cards rise. Just push them up from the back of the deck.

Ice Water

Pour a little water into a paper cup. Say you will make the water disappear. Ask someone to hold out a hand. Pour the cup into it.

The person expects to get wet. An ICE CUBE falls out instead. Say that you tried to make the water disappear — but it was too HARD!

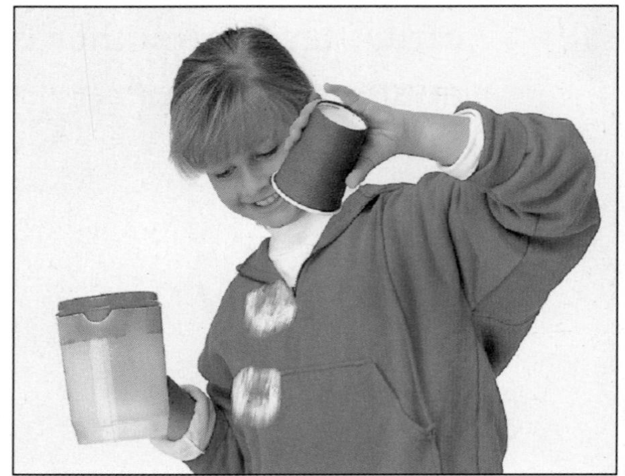

How Is It Done?

This trick is very easy to do. You will need a piece of dry sponge. Cut it into a round shape so that it fits into your cup. Glue it to the bottom.

Put an ice cube into the cup. Have another cup of water handy. Now you are ready. Pour a little water into the cup. (The sponge soaks it right up.) Pour the ice cube out onto someone's hand. What a surprise!

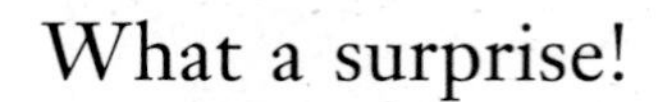

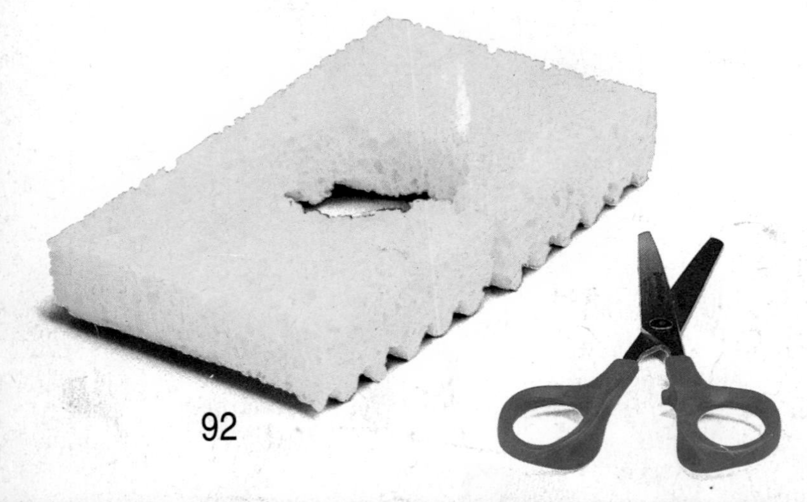

TRICK NOTEBOOK

Now that you have read about a number of magic tricks, make a notebook of some of your favorites. You can include the tricks of Harry Kellar and Houdini as well as some of the tricks in this selection. You might also include tricks from other magic books.

Describe how each trick is done and include drawings, if you wish.

MEET THE AUTHORS

Anne Edwards

Anne Edwards began her career as a movie and television writer in Hollywood. She is the author of many books; this is her second book for children.

Robert Kraske

Robert Kraske has spent many years writing magazine articles and books for children. He has written about Harry Houdini and other famous daredevils, life in outer space, pirates, the Statue of Liberty, and many other topics.

Ray Broekel

One of Ray Broekel's favorite hobbies is magic. He enjoys doing magic tricks and uses them when he talks to elementary schoolchildren about writing. With Laurence B. White, Jr., he wrote many easy magic books for beginners. He has also written books for children about sports, science, and careers.

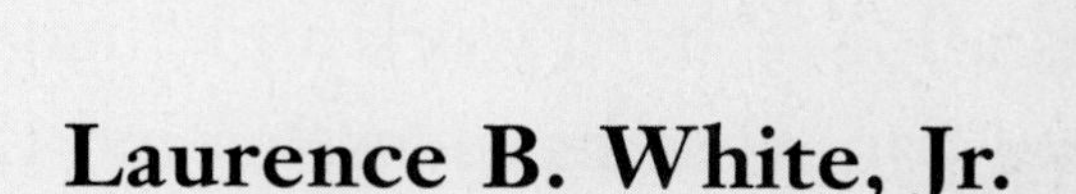

Laurence B. White, Jr.

Laurence B. White, Jr., says he "caught the magic bug" in first grade. As a child, he took magic lessons from a local magician. While in college, he earned money doing magic shows. As an author, White is especially interested in sharing his love of magic with children. Look through his books, and you may catch the magic bug too!

Reading Is Magic

Theater Magic
by Cheryl Walsh Bellville

When a professional children's theater performs Hans Christian Andersen's *The Nightingale,* it takes a lot of hard work and "magic." This book shows you what happens behind the curtain.

Magic: An Introduction
by Betty and Douglas Kobs

Watch Mysto the magician make paper clips jump and do the Magic Scissors trick. Learn these tricks and more.

Soap Bubble Magic
by Seymour Simon

Soap bubbles can be magical. Try some of these simple experiments. Can you hold a bubble in your hand?

The Mickey Mouse Magic Book
by Walt Disney Productions

First, make a magic wand. Next, say the magic words. Now you're ready to make a penny appear and to do other tricks.

THEATER
MAGIC
Behind the Scenes at a Children's Theater
by Cheryl Walsh Bellville
AWARD EDITION
HOUGHTON MIFFLIN
The Literature Experience
READING
magic
An Introduction

Meet Jack Prelutsky

When you read the poetry of Jack Prelutsky, you'll find silly situations, meet creepy creatures, and read menus of strange foods. But his poems are not all nonsense. Jack Prelutsky also writes about real life — making friends, dealing with bullies, feeling glad, mad, or sad.

Jack Prelutsky is known for his rollicking rhymes and rhythms. His poems sound like songs that make you want to sing along. In fact, Prelutsky started out as a singer of folk songs. He writes with a guitar nearby. Sometimes he makes up a tune and sings a poem to see if the rhythm works.

Besides writing poetry, Jack Prelutsky likes to make wooden toys and metal sculpture, collect books and models of frogs, invent word games, and ride a bicycle.

As you read these poems, see what else you can learn about Jack Prelutsky.

I'M IN A ROTTEN MOOD!

I'm in a rotten mood today,
a really rotten mood today,
I'm feeling cross,
I'm feeling mean,
I'm jumpy as a jumping bean,
I have an awful attitude –
I'M IN A ROTTEN MOOD!

I'm in a rotten mood today,
a really rotten mood today,
I'm in a snit,
I'm in a stew,
there's nothing that I care to do
but sit all by myself and brood –
I'M IN A ROTTEN MOOD!

I'm in a rotten mood today,
a really rotten mood today,
you'd better stay away from me,
I'm just a lump of misery,
I'm feeling absolutely rude –
I'M IN A ROTTEN MOOD!

GRASSHOPPER GUMBO

GRASSHOPPER GUMBO
IGUANA TAIL TARTS
TOAD À LA MODE
PICKLED PELICAN PARTS
ELEPHANT GELATIN
FROG FRICASSEE
PURÉE OF PLATYPUS
BOILED BUMBLEBEE
PORCUPINE PUDDING
STEAMED CENTIPEDE SKINS
SQUID SUCKER SUNDAES
FRIED FLYING FISH FINS
MEADOW MOUSE MORSELS
CRACKED CROCODILE CRUNCH

The school cafeteria
serves them for lunch.

THE NEW KID ON THE BLOCK

There's a new kid on the block,
and boy, that kid is tough,
that new kid punches hard,
that new kid plays real rough,
that new kid's big and strong,
with muscles everywhere,
that new kid tweaked my arm,
that new kid pulled my hair.

That new kid likes to fight,
and picks on all the guys,
that new kid scares me some,
(that new kid's twice my size),
that new kid stomped my toes,
that new kid swiped my ball,
that new kid's really bad,
I don't care for her at all.

I AM A GHOST WHO'S LOST HIS BOO

I am a ghost who's lost his boo,
my boo is gone from me,
and I'm without a single clue
to where my boo might be.
It makes me mope, it makes me pout,
it almost makes me moan,
a ghost is not a ghost without
a boo to call his own.

My boo was piercing, fierce, and loud,
I used to strut and boast,
for I was positively proud
to be a gruesome ghost.
But now that I'm without a boo,
I find it rather weird,
there's little for a ghost to do
whose boo has disappeared.

Although I hover here and there,
and haunt a hundred rooms,
it seems there's no one I can scare
unless my boo resumes.
I am a ghost who's lost his boo,
alas! A boo I lack,
if you should find my boo, then you
had better give it back.

REGION

THEME 3

A VISIT TO THE SOUTHWEST

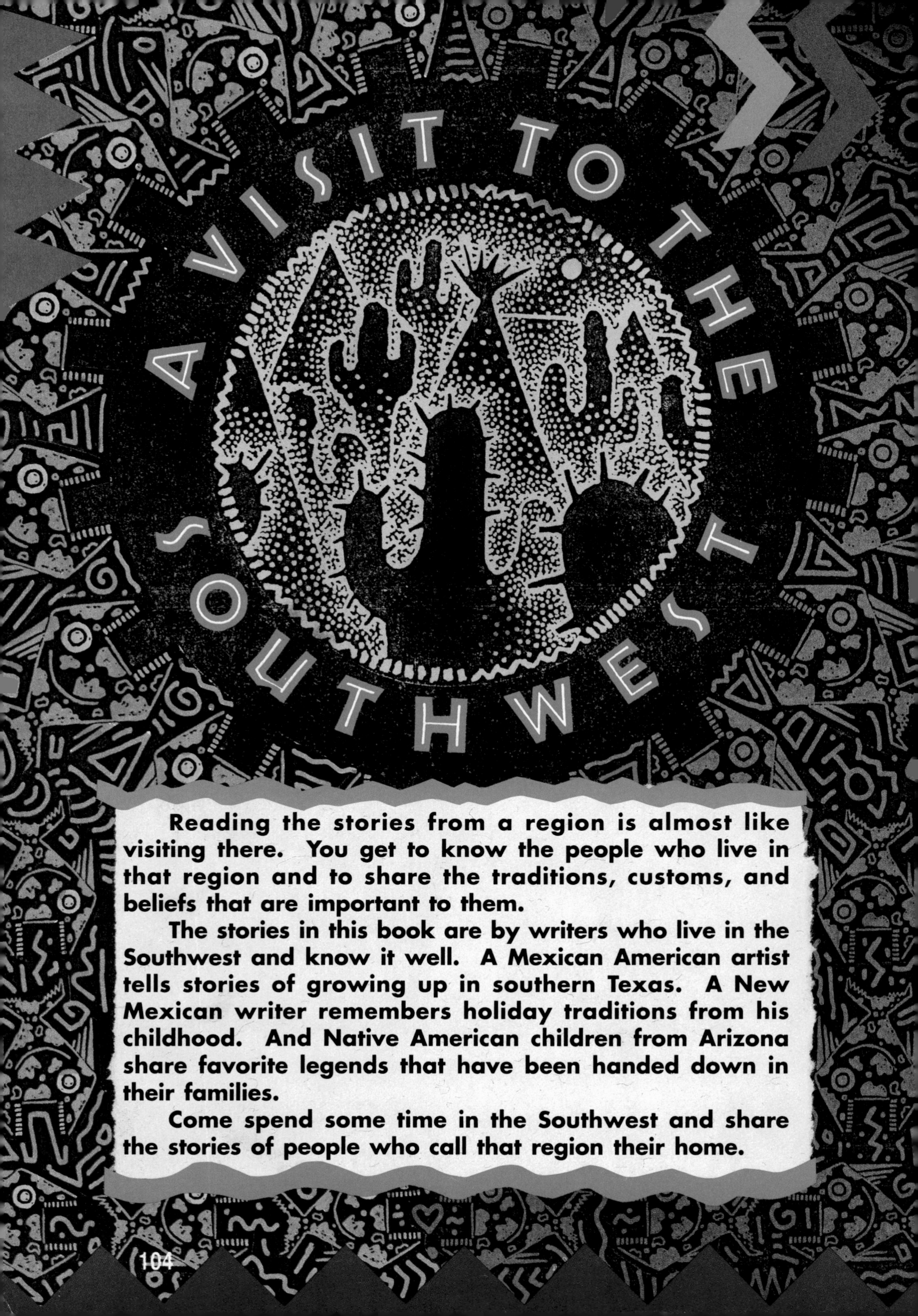

A Visit to the Southwest

Reading the stories from a region is almost like visiting there. You get to know the people who live in that region and to share the traditions, customs, and beliefs that are important to them.

The stories in this book are by writers who live in the Southwest and know it well. A Mexican American artist tells stories of growing up in southern Texas. A New Mexican writer remembers holiday traditions from his childhood. And Native American children from Arizona share favorite legends that have been handed down in their families.

Come spend some time in the Southwest and share the stories of people who call that region their home.

CONTENTS

FAMILY CUADROS DE FAMILIA PICTURES

STORIES AND PAINTINGS
BY CARMEN LOMAS GARZA

The pictures in this book are all painted from my memories of growing up in Kingsville, Texas, near the border with Mexico. From the time I was a young girl I always dreamed of becoming an artist. I practiced drawing every day; I studied art in school; and I finally did become an artist. My family has inspired and encouraged me for all these years. This is my book of family pictures.

Los cuadros de este libro los pinté de los recuerdos de mi niñez en Kingsville, Texas, cerca de la frontera con México. Desde que era pequeña, siempre soñé con ser artista. Dibujaba cada día; estudié arte en la escuela; y por fin, me hice artista. Mi familia me ha inspirado y alentado todos estos años. Este es mi libro de cuadros de familia.

THE FAIR IN REYNOSA

My friends and I once went to a very big fair across the border in Reynosa, Mexico. The fair lasted a whole week. Artisans and entertainers came from all over Mexico. There were lots of booths with food and crafts. This is one little section where everybody is ordering and eating tacos.

I painted a father buying tacos and the rest of the family sitting down at the table. The little girl is the father's favorite and that's why she gets to tag along with him. I can always recognize little girls who are their fathers' favorites.

LA FERIA EN REYNOSA

Una vez, mis amigos y yo fuimos a una feria muy grande en Reynosa, México, al otro lado de la frontera. La feria duró una semana entera. Vinieron artesanos y artistas de todo México. Había muchos puestos que vendían comida y artesanías. Ésta es una pequeña parte de la feria donde todos están comprando tacos y comiéndoselos.

Pinté a un padre comprando tacos y al resto de la familia sentada a la mesa. La niñita pequeña es la preferida de su papá, y por eso es que él la permite acompañarlo. Aún hoy, siempre puedo reconocer cuando una niñita es la preferida de su papá.

SODAS
CocaCola
Fresa
Limon
$5.00 pesos
CARNE ASADA
Con Tomate y Salsa
$12.00 pesos
CARMEN LOMAS GARZA
©1987
La feria en Reynosa

ORANGES

We were always going to my grandparents' house, so whatever they were involved in we would get involved in. In this picture my grandmother is hanging up the laundry. We told her that the oranges needed picking so she said, "Well, go ahead and pick some." Before she knew it, she had too many oranges to hold in her hands, so she made a basket out of her apron. That's my brother up in the tree, picking oranges. The rest of us are picking up the ones that he dropped on the ground.

NARANJAS

Siempre íbamos a la casa de mis abuelos, así que cualquier cosa que estuvieran haciendo ellos, nosotros la hacíamos también. En este cuadro, mi abuela está colgando la ropa a secar. Nosotros le dijimos que las naranjas estaban listas para cosechar, y ella nos respondió: —Vayan pues, recójanlas. En un dos por tres, tenía demasiadas naranjas para sostenerlas en las manos, así que convirtió su delantal en canasta. Ése es mi hermano, en el árbol, recogiendo naranjas. El resto de nosotros estamos recogiendo las que él deja caer al suelo.

CARMEN LOMAS GARZA
©1988

FOR DINNER

This is my grandparents' backyard. My grandmother is killing a chicken for dinner. My grandfather is in the chicken coop trying to catch another chicken. Later, my family will sit down to eat Sunday dinner — chicken soup.

That's me in the blue dress with my younger brother, Arturo. He was so surprised by the scene that he started to spill his snowcone. We had never seen anything like that before. I knew my grandparents had always raised chickens, but I never knew how the chickens got to be soup.

PARA LA CENA

Éste es el patio de mis abuelos. Mi abuela está matando a una gallina para la cena. Mi abuelo está en el gallinero tratando de atrapar a otra gallina. Más tarde, mi familia se sentará a comer la cena del domingo: sopa de pollo.

Ésa soy yo, vestida de azul, con mi hermano menor, Arturo. Él estaba tan sorprendido por lo que veía que se le empezó a derramar su raspa. Nunca antes habíamos visto algo parecido. Yo sabía que mis abuelos criaban gallinas, pero no había sabido antes cómo era que las gallinas se convertían en sopa.

CARMEN LOMAS GARZA
©1986

BIRTHDAY PARTY

That's me hitting the piñata at my sixth birthday party. It was also my brother's fourth birthday. My mother made a big birthday party for us and invited all kinds of friends, cousins and neighborhood kids.

You can't see the piñata when you're trying to hit it, because your eyes are covered with a handkerchief. My father is pulling the rope that makes the piñata go up and down. He will make sure that everybody has a chance to hit it at least once. Somebody will end up breaking it, and that's when all the candies will fall out and all the kids will run and try to grab them.

CUMPLEAÑOS

Ésa soy yo, pegándole a la piñata en la fiesta que me dieron cuando cumplí seis años. Era también el cumpleaños de mi hermano, que cumplía cuatro años. Mi madre nos dio una gran fiesta e invitó a muchos primos, vecinos y amigos.

No puedes ver la piñata cuando le estás dando con el palo, porque tienes los ojos cubiertos por un pañuelo. Mi padre está tirando de la cuerda que sube y baja la piñata. Él se encargará de que todos tengan por lo menos una oportunidad de pegarle a la piñata. Luego alguien acabará rompiéndola, y entonces todos los caramelos que tiene dentro caerán y todos los niños correrán a cogerlos.

Happy Birthday
Carmen
CARMEN LOMAS GARZA

CAKEWALK

Cakewalk was a game to raise money to send Mexican Americans to the university. You paid 25 cents to stand on a number. When the music started, you walked around and around. When the music stopped, whatever number you happened to step on was your number. Then one of the ladies in the center would pick out a number from the can. If you were standing on the winning number, you would win a cake. That's my mother in the center of the circle in the pink and black dress. My father is serving punch. I'm the little girl in front of the store scribbling on the sidewalk with a twig.

CAKEWALK

Cakewalk era un juego que se hacía para recaudar fondos para darles becas universitarias a jóvenes méxico-americanos. Se pagaba 25 centavos para poder pararse sobre un número. Cuando la música empezaba a tocar, todos empezaban a caminar en círculo. Cuando se terminaba la música, el número sobre el cual estabas parado era tu número. Entonces una de las señoras que estaba en el centro del círculo escogía un número de la lata. Si estabas parado sobre el número de la suerte, ganabas un pastel. Ésa es mi madre en el centro del círculo, vestida de rosado y negro. Mi papá esta sirviendo ponche. Yo soy la niñita dibujando garabatos en la acera al frente de la tienda con una ramita.

Notario Público
Rainbow Bread
Rainbow Bread
MATILDE'S GRO.
Yerbas Piñatas
OJAS

PICKING NOPAL CACTUS

In the early spring my grandfather would come and get us and we'd all go out into the woods to pick nopal cactus. My grandfather and my mother are slicing off the fresh, tender leaves of the nopal and putting them in boxes. My grandmother and my brother Arturo are pulling leaves from the mesquite tree to line the boxes. After we got home my grandfather would shave off all the needles from each leaf of cactus. Then my grandmother would parboil the leaves in hot water. The next morning she would cut them up and stir fry them with chili powder and eggs for breakfast.

PISCANDO NOPALITOS

Al comienzo de la primavera, mi abuelo nos venía a buscar y todos íbamos al bosque a piscar nopalitos. Mi abuelo y mi madre están cortando las pencas tiernas del nopal y metiéndolas en cajas. Mi abuela y mi hermano Arturo están recogiendo hojas de mesquite para forrar las cajas. Después que regresábamos a casa, mi abuelo le quitaba las espinas a cada penca del cactus. Luego mi abuela cocía las pencas en agua hirviente. A la mañana siguiente, las cortaba y las freía con chile y huevos para nuestro desayuno.

HAMMERHEAD SHARK

This picture is about the times my family went to Padre Island in the Gulf of Mexico to go swimming. Once when we got there, a fisherman had just caught a big hammerhead shark at the end of the pier. How he got the shark to the beach, I never found out. It was scary to see because it was big enough to swallow a little kid whole.

TIBURÓN MARTILLO

Este cuadro trata de las veces que mi familia iba a nadar a la Isla del Padre en el Golfo de México. Una vez cuando llegamos, un pescador acababa de atrapar a un tiburón martillo al cabo del muelle. Cómo logró llevar al tiburón a la playa, nunca me enteré. Daba mucho miedo ver al tiburón, porque era tan grande que hubiera podido tragarse a un niño pequeño de un solo bocado.

RABBIT

My grandfather used to have a garden and also raise chickens and rabbits. In this painting, he is coming into the kitchen with a freshly prepared rabbit for dinner. My grandmother is making tortillas. That's my little brother, Arturo, sitting on the bench. He liked to watch my grandmother cook. And that's my younger sister, Margie, playing jacks on the floor. I'm watching from my grandparents' bedroom which is next to the kitchen.

CONEJO

Mi abuelo tenía un jardín, y también criaba pollos y conejos. En este cuadro, está entrando a la cocina con un conejo que acaba de preparar para la cena. Mi abuelita está preparando tortillas. Ése es mi hermano Arturo, sentado en la banca. Le gustaba mirar a mi abuela mientras cocinaba. Y ésa es mi hermana menor, Margie, jugando a los "jacks" en el suelo. Yo estoy mirando desde la recámara de mis abuelos, que está al lado de la cocina.

LA MEXICANA
S
P

JOSEPH AND MARY SEEKING SHELTER AT THE INN

On each of the nine nights before Christmas we act out the story of Mary and Joseph seeking shelter at the inn. We call this custom "Las Posadas." A little girl and a little boy play Mary and Joseph and they are led by an angel.

Each night the travelers go to a different house. They knock on the door. When the door opens, they sing: "We are Mary and Joseph looking for shelter." At first the family inside refuses to let them in; then the travelers sing again. At last Joseph and Mary are let into the house. Then everybody comes in and we have a party.

LAS POSADAS

Cada una de las nueve noches antes de Nochebuena, representamos la historia de María y José buscando albergue en la posada. Esta costumbre se llama "Las Posadas". Una niñita y un niñito representan a María y José, y hay un ángel que les guía.

Cada noche, los caminantes van a una casa distinta. Tocan la puerta. Cuando la puerta se abre, cantan: —Somos María y José, buscando posada. Al principio la familia no los deja entrar; entonces los caminantes vuelven a cantar. Por fin dejan entrar a María y José. Luego todos entran y celebran con una fiesta.

MAKING TAMALES

This is a scene from my parents' kitchen. Everybody is making tamales. My grandfather is wearing blue overalls and a blue shirt. I'm right next to him with my sister Margie. We're helping to soak the dried leaves from the corn. My mother is spreading the cornmeal dough on the leaves and my aunt and uncle are spreading meat on the dough. My grandmother is lining up the rolled and folded tamales ready for cooking. In some families just the women make tamales, but in our family everybody helps.

LA TAMALADA

Ésta es una escena de la cocina de mis padres. Todos están haciendo tamales. Mi abuelo tiene puesto rancheros azules y camisa azul. Yo estoy al lado de él, con mi hermana Margie. Estamos ayudando a remojar las hojas secas del maíz. Mi Mamá está esparciendo la masa de maíz sobre las hojas, y mis tíos están esparciendo la carne sobre la masa. Mi abuelita está ordenando los tamales que ya están enrollados, cubiertos y listos para cocer. En algunas familias sólo las mujeres preparan tamales, pero en mi familia todos ayudan.

OJAS
CARMEN LOMAS GARZA
©1987
TAMALADA

WATERMELON

It's a hot summer evening. The whole family's on the front porch. My grandfather had brought us some watermelons that afternoon. We put them in the refrigerator and let them chill down. After supper we went out to the front porch. My father cut the watermelon and gave each one of us a slice.

It was fun to sit out there. The light was so bright on the porch that you couldn't see beyond the edge of the lit area. It was like being in our own little world.

SANDÍA

Es una noche calurosa de verano. Toda la familia está en el corredor. Mi abuelo nos había traído unas sandías esa tarde. Las pusimos en el refrigerador para enfriarlas. Despues de la cena, salimos al corredor. Mi padre cortó la sandía y nos dio un pedazo a cada uno.

Era divertido estar sentados allá afuera. La luz del corredor era tan fuerte que no se podía ver más allá del área que estaba iluminada. Era como estar en nuestro propio pequeño mundo.

CARMEN
LOMAS
GARZA
©1986

THE VIRGIN OF SAN JUAN

A mother and son have gone to church and she's doing some praying. In the meantime, her son starts entertaining himself by taking things out of her purse. She lets him for a while. Then he hands her a handkerchief. I don't know if he thought that maybe she was crying and needed her handkerchief, or whether he was just playing with it and she took it away from him.

LA VIRGEN DE SAN JUAN

Una madre y su hijo han ido a la iglesia y ella está rezando. Mientras tanto, el hijo se entretiene sacando cosas de su cartera. Ella se lo permite por un rato. Luego él le entrega un pañuelo. No sé si es que el niño pensó que su madre estaba llorando y necesitaba su pañuelo, o si el niño estaba jugando con el pañuelo y su madre se lo quitó.

CARMEN LOMAS GARZA
©1985

HEALER

This is a scene at a neighbor's house. The lady in bed was very sick with the flu. She had already been to a regular doctor and had gotten prescription drugs for her chest cold. But she had also asked a healer, a curandera, to do a final cleansing or healing for this flu. So the curandera came over and did a cleansing using branches from the rue tree. She also burned copal incense in a coffee can at the foot of the bed. Curanderas know a lot about healing. They are very highly respected.

CURANDERA

Ésta es una escena en la casa de una vecina. La mujer que está en cama estaba muy enferma con influenza. Ya había visto a un doctor y había conseguido una receta médica para sus pulmones. Pero también le había pedido a una curandera que le hiciera una limpieza final o cura para su enfermedad. Así que la curandera vino e hizo una limpieza usando ramas de ruda. También quemó incienso de copal en una lata de café al pie de la cama. Las curanderas saben mucho y ayudan mucho a la gente. Por eso se las respeta tanto.

CARMEN LOMAS GARZA ©
"CURANDERA"

BEDS FOR DREAMING

My sister and I used to go up on the roof on summer nights and just stay there and talk about the stars and the constellations. We also talked about the future. I knew since I was 13 years old that I wanted to be an artist. And all those things that I dreamed of doing as an artist, I'm finally doing now. My mother was the one who inspired me to be an artist. She made up our beds to sleep in and have regular dreams, but she also laid out the bed for our dreams of the future.

CAMAS PARA SOÑAR

Mi hermana y yo solíamos subirnos al techo en las noches de verano y nos quedábamos allí platicando sobre las estrellas y las constelaciones. También platicábamos del futuro. Yo sabía desde que tenía trece años que quería ser artista. Y todas las cosas que soñaba hacer como artista, por fin las estoy haciendo ahora. Mi madre fue la que me inspiró a ser artista. Ella nos tendía las camas para que durmiéramos y tuviéramos sueños normales, pero también preparó la cuna para nuestros sueños del futuro.

CARMEN
LOMAS
GARZA

MAKE YOUR OWN FAMILY PICTURES

Carmen Lomas Garza told about her childhood in a small Texas town using stories and pictures. Now it's your turn to make a book of family pictures that shows scenes from your life. Draw pictures of times you shared with your family. Then write a paragraph about each picture. Tell who is in the picture, what is happening, and why it was an important time for you. When you finish, share your family pictures with a classmate.

CARMEN LOMAS GARZA

For her book *Family Pictures,* Carmen Lomas Garza painted pictures about her family and the traditional Hispanic community where she grew up. As a young girl in Kingsville, Texas, she dreamed of someday becoming an artist. Today the dream she whispered to her sister on the roof of their house has come true. She is now considered one of the finest Mexican American painters. Her paintings have been shown in California, Texas, and Arizona, as well as New York and Chicago. *Family Pictures* is her first book.

RUDOLFO A. ANAYA

"I grew up in a small town in New Mexico called Santa Rosa," says Rudolfo Anaya. "The Pecos River flows through it, and as a boy I spent hours playing along the banks of that river."

Anaya remembers visits to his home from relatives and neighbors who would tell stories in Spanish for hours on end. "During those visits, all these stories would just flow out of people. That richness of stories was important in my life."

Anaya wrote *The Farolitos of Christmas,* which was set in the early 1940's, for his granddaughter, Kristan. He wanted to explain the tradition of the farolitos to her. Today when he tells the story of the farolitos to schoolchildren, he says, "they are then anxious to tell me about the traditions in their families. 'Here's what *we* do,' the children will say. They become the storytellers. I've heard some amazing stories from them!"

THE FAROLITOS OF CHRISTMAS

A NEW MEXICO CHRISTMAS STORY

BY

RUDOLFO A. ANAYA

ILLUSTRATED BY RICHARD SANDOVAL

GLOSSARY

abuelo (ah•BWAY•loe) grandfather

atole (ah•TOE•lay) a hot cereal made from blue cornmeal

biscochitos (BEEZ•ko•CHEE•toes) sugar cookies

buenos días (BWAY•nose DEE•ahs) salutation: good day

empanaditas (em•pah•nah•DEE•tas) little pies stuffed with sweet meat and deep fried

farol (fah•ROLL) lantern

farolito (fah•roll•LEE•toe) small lantern

Felíz Navidad (fay•LEEZ nah•VEE•dahd) Merry Christmas

luminarias (loo•mee•NAH•ree•ahs) small bonfires of stacked wood

mamá (mah•MAH) mother

mi'jita (mee•HEE•tah) my daughter

nacimiento (nah•CEE•mee•en•toe) Nativity scene

oshá (oh•SHAH) an herb used for medicinal purposes

papá (pah•PAH) father

pastores (pahs•TORE•ess) shepherds

posole (poh•SOUL•lay) a stew made with pork, hominy and chile

San Miguel (sahn MEE•ghel) St. Michael

Santo Niño (sahn•toe NEE•nyo) baby Jesus

It was going to be a sad Christmas, Luz thought as she hurried down the road to the house of her friend Reina. Only three days to Christmas and her father still had not returned home, and worst of all, her grandfather was ill.

"Caw. Caw," the black crow called from the bare branches of the cottonwood tree.

To Luz, his cry sounded like "Cold. Cold."

She paused to look at the large, black bird. "Yes, Mr. Crow," she said aloud, "it is a cold morning."

Luz tightly grasped the gifts she was taking to school. Then she snuggled her chin down into her scarf and walked on.

Except for a few children hurrying to school, the streets of the village were empty. The men had already gone to work, and the women were cooking and cleaning in the warm houses. Everyone was preparing for Christmas.

There was frost on the ground, and a cold wind blew through the bare trees. Luz looked at the Sangre de Cristo Mountains. Gray clouds covered the tall peaks.

Perhaps it will snow for Christmas, Luz thought. As she turned the corner at the grocery store, she stopped to look at the cardboard figure of Santa Claus in the window. Drink Coca Cola the sign said.

"Qué bonito," she said aloud. "He looks like an old grandfather."

"Santo Clos," her grandfather called Santa.

"Is Santo Clos real?" Luz had asked her grandfather one day.

"Oh yes, he's real," her *abuelo* winked. "He comes with his bag full of presents for the children. But the *pastores* come to adore and sing to the *Santo Niño*."

"Tell me about the pastores, abuelo," Luz said. She knew the pastores were people from the village who dressed as shepherds on Christmas Eve. They performed the story of the original shepherds who had gone to see the birth of Christ.

"The pastores are an old tradition," her abuelo said. "They have been part of Christmas for hundreds of years. And the pastores of San Juan are the best in all New Mexico. On Christmas Eve when they come down the road on their way to church, they stop to present their play in front of the house with the brightest *luminarias*."

"And that's our house, abuelo!" Luz said eagerly.

"Yes. You and I make the luminarias, the little stacks of wood in two lines, right to our door. On Christmas Eve we light the wood, and everyone comes to see the bonfires. Then the pastores stop at our house and sing. After they sing and tell the story of the shepherds going to see the birth of Jesus, we will invite them in to eat."

Her abuelo had lighted the luminarias every Christmas Eve since Luz could remember. Now he was sick with a terrible cold and the doctor wouldn't let him work outside. There would be no luminarias this Christmas. The pastores would not stop to sing in front of Luz's house.

Luz worried. What was Christmas without the pastores coming to their home to sing?

Luz heard the school bell ring as she hurried to Reina's house. They didn't want to be late for school or Mrs. Smith, their fourth-grade teacher, would make them stand in the corner.

Luz knocked on the door and Reina ran out, her arms full of presents to take to school. She wore a bright red woven jacket and warm mittens. Her mother was one of the best weavers in the pueblo.

"Good morning, Luz!" Reina called.

"Hi, Reina. Let me help." She took one of Reina's packages. "What's the yarn for?" she asked. Reina held strands of brightly colored yarn.

"For the Christmas tree at school," Reina said.

"Oh, it will be beautiful," Luz smiled.

"Good morning, Luz," Reina's mother called from the door. "How's your mom?"

"Buenos días," Luz answered. "She's fine, thank you."

"And your grandfather?"

"He still has to stay in bed. His cough is worse."

"Tell him to take tea of *oshá*. I'll send some with you this afternoon. That will help."

"Thank you, Mrs. Abeyta."

Reina's mother said goodbye, and the two girls hurried towards the school.

"We are going to decorate the Christmas tree at school," Reina said. "Isn't that exciting!"

"Yes," Luz nodded. "We don't have a Christmas tree at home."

"We usually celebrate Christmas by going to the other pueblos to dance," Reina said, "but my father said maybe this year we could have a tree. Could you come over and help me decorate it?"

"Yes," Luz nodded.

"My father said he will cut a star of tin for the top of the tree."

"It will be beautiful," Luz said.

"Is your father coming home for Christmas?" Reina asked.

"He's working far away," Luz said, "and we don't know if he will be home in time for Christmas."

"I'm sorry, Luz."

"Anyway, I don't need a Christmas tree. My abuelo and I make the luminarias for the pastores."

"I like the pastores best of all," Reina said. "I like Bartolo. He's the clown."

"I like Gila. She sings beautifully. Mother said when I grow up, maybe I can be Gila."

"It's my favorite story," said Reina.

"Mine, too," Luz said quietly.

"Luz. You sound so sad. Is it because your abuelo is sick?"

Luz stopped and looked at her friend. Tears filled her eyes.

"Abuelo has been sick for a long time," Luz said. "The doctor said it is a bad cold. Now he can't do any hard work. He can't cut the wood to make luminarias. He can't even cut wood for the stove. He's so sad."

"I'm sorry, Luz. I wish there was something we could do."

"There's nothing anyone can do," Luz said. She wiped the tears from her eyes. "Come on, we don't want to be late for school."

She turned and ran into the school so Reina wouldn't see her cry.

At school that day they decorated the Christmas tree and painted pictures of Santa Claus with his big bag of presents. Mrs. Smith taught them "Silent Night, Holy Night."

While they were singing, Luz thought of her abuelo and wished he would get well so they could light the luminarias for the shepherds.

That afternoon Luz and Reina hurried home from school. Reina's mother gave Luz the oshá to take home to her abuelo. She also sent warm bread from the oven and a dozen freshly baked tamales to Luz's mother.

"Thank you," Luz said. Then she said goodbye to Reina and hurried home.

At home her mother was baking *empanaditas,* little pies stuffed with sweet meat. The kitchen smelled delicious. Abuelo sat napping near the stove. The cat lay quietly on his lap.

"Luz, I'm glad you're home. How was school?" her mother asked.

"It was fine," Luz said and took off her jacket. "We decorated the Christmas tree, and we sang, and then we exchanged presents. Mrs. Smith said to say thank you for the cookies you sent her. How is abuelo?" She looked at her grandfather.

"He's feeling better today," her mother said.

"Reina's mother sent some oshá."

Her mother helped her make tea from the oshá. When it was ready, Luz took a cup of the tea to her grandfather. She touched his arm.

"Abuelo, I'm home."

Her abuelo opened his eyes. "Luz *mi'jita.* I am glad to see you. I fell asleep — I was dreaming. In my dream I saw the pastores coming to our home. I heard the shepherds singing about the newborn child in Bethlehem. I saw *San Miguel,* the archangel, leading the pastores to the manger."

"It was a beautiful dream," Luz said, "because in the end the pastores do get to Bethlehem in time for the birth of Jesus."

She kissed her grandfather's cheek. "Look, I made you some tea from oshá for your cough." She handed him the cup of tea and sat by his side. He smelled warm and strong. When she was by his side, she didn't feel sad anymore.

Abuelo sipped the tea. "Ah, this is better than the doctor's medicine," he said. "With this tea I will get better. Soon I will feel strong enough to cut the wood for the luminarias. I have to get them ready for the pastores."

Luz looked at her mother. Her mother didn't know what to say. They both knew the doctor had said that abuelo would not be able to do any work until after Christmas. There would be no luminarias for Christmas.

That afternoon Luz went to Reina's house. Reina's father had brought a small, green tree from the mountains. Luz helped Reina decorate it. They tied popcorn chains and brightly colored yarn on the tree. Reina's mother put a white wool blanket around the bottom of the tree to look like snow. Finally, Reina's father tied the star to the top of the tree.

When they were finished, they stood back and admired their work.

"Our first Christmas tree," Reina cried.

"When we were little, we didn't have Christmas trees," her mother said.

"And no Santa Claus?" Reina asked.

"No."

"What did you do for Christmas?" Luz asked.

"We visited family and friends. We took food to the old people. The people here in the pueblo held a Deer Dance after they went to church."

"And the pastores," Luz said.

"Ever since I can remember, the pastores have come to your grandfather's house," Reina's mother said. "It's the most beautiful part of Christmas."

And this year we won't have them, Luz thought sadly.

There was no school the following day. Luz swept the house while her mother made tamales and *posole,* a stew made of hominy, pork and chile. Abuelo puttered around the kitchen, trying to help. There would be no pastores this year, but they would have plenty of food for family and neighbors who came to visit. And they would take food to the old people of the village. It was a tradition for everyone in the village of San Juan to share what they had.

In the afternoon Reina came to visit. She and Luz decorated the sill of the front window with small candles.

"We will light them Christmas Eve," Luz's mother said. "From the road the people will see the candles burning. Maybe the pastores will stop as they pass."

"I think not," abuelo said. "If there are no luminarias, they will not stop."

"Maybe we could place a row of candles outside," Reina said. "The candles will be the luminarias."

"Good idea," Luz agreed. "How many candles do we have, *mamá*?"

"Oh, I have dozens," her mother said. "I bought three boxes so I would have enough to take to church."

"Then let's make a row of them!" Luz said. "Like Reina said. From our door all the way to the street. The candles will be our luminarias!"

Mother looked at abuelo. He laughed and shook his head. "Look," he said and pointed out the window. "See those clouds in the mountains? That means it will snow on Christmas Eve. The wind and the snow will put out the candles. That is why I use the piles of piñón wood as luminarias. Not even snow and wind can put out the bonfires when I start them. If it snows, the pastores can still come and sing and tell their story. The people who come to watch the play can warm themselves by the fires. The tradition goes on because the fires are strong. But candles? No. The snow and wind would put them out."

He shook his head sadly and went back to his chair by the stove.

"Maybe we could put the candles in cans," Luz said. "Then the wind wouldn't blow them out."

"Then we couldn't see the light of the candles," her mother said.

Luz sighed. She looked at Reina. Reina didn't know what to do either. There would be no luminarias this Christmas Eve, and the pastores would not stop. They would not be invited in to share the feast of tamales, posole, hot chocolate and *biscochitos.*

All afternoon Luz looked at the candles and thought of what to do.

If only I had something to put them in, Luz thought. Then I could make a line of the candles and light them for the pastores. That would make abuelo happy.

Just before dinner Luz's mother called her.

"Can you run to the store before it gets dark and get some sugar? I used it all today baking the biscochitos."

Luz put on her coat and mittens, kissed her mother and abuelo and ran out into the cold. The wind was

ICE CREAM
Sugar
flour

beginning to blow — there were wisps of snow in the air. Light glowed from the windows of the village. Everyone was at supper. By morning the village would be covered by a blanket of snow. It would be a white Christmas.

Luz entered the store and bought the sugar for her mother. The storekeeper put the sugar in a brown paper bag. Luz thanked him and started home. She was still thinking of a way to use the candles to make the luminarias.

She paused and looked at the windows of the houses. The sun had set, the windows looked so warm and cheery.

"The candles need a house, to protect them from the wind," Luz thought. "But what will hold the candle in place and still let it glow?"

Luz didn't know.

When she got home, she handed her mother the bag of sugar.

"Thank you, Luz," her mother said. "I had no sugar left for your abuelo's coffee." She emptied the sugar in her sugar can and handed Luz the bag. "Will you please put this away?"

Luz took the bag. She saved all the paper bags in a special place in the pantry. Once a month she took them back to the store and the storekeeper gave her a penny for the bags. Then Luz could buy whatever she wanted with her penny. Sometimes she bought candy, sometimes gum.

Luz started to fold the bag, but stopped. What if she placed the candle in the bag? The candle would glow. Yes, she thought. It would. Her heart beat faster. She ran to her abuelo.

"¡Abuelo! We can put the candles in bags! That way they will shine and not go out!"

Her grandfather looked up from his newspaper.

"What?" he asked.

"We can put a candle in each bag and make luminarias!"

She handed her abuelo the bag and ran to get one of the small candles. "See, like this." She placed the open bag on the table and put the small candle in the bag.

"Now we light it," she said. She felt her heart racing. It would work, she thought, it would work.

Her abuelo took his glasses off. He got up slowly and looked at the candle in the bag. Her mother stopped setting the dishes and looked at the bag.

"Luz, I don't think it will work," she said. "The wind will blow the bag away."

"If there was sugar in the bag, it wouldn't fall," Luz said. She took a cupful of sugar and put it in the bag. Then she set the candle in the sugar.

"But we can't use that much sugar," her mother said.

"Wait," abuelo said. "She has a good idea. We can use sand in the bag, not sugar."

He took a match from his pocket and lighted it by scratching it with his thumbnail. Then he lit the candle inside the bag. It sputtered, then glowed brightly. The three stood looking at the warm glow of the candle. The light seemed to dance inside the bag.

"It looks like a *farol,* a lantern," her abuelo said. "You have made a beautiful *farolito*. That's what we will call it, a farolito. Take it outside to see it glow in the dark."

Luz tenderly picked up the bag with the lighted candle while her mother opened the door. She and abuelo stood

at the door while Luz walked out into the night. In the dark, the candle in the brown paper bag glowed brightly.

"Oh, it is beautiful," Luz's mother said.

"Imagine a hundred of them," abuelo said. "All along the path to the road, on top of the adobe wall, shining to light the way for the pastores."

"And the children can make them," the mother said. "It will truly be a child's Christmas."

Luz ran back to her mother and abuelo. The three stood huddled at the door, looking at the farolito that glowed brightly in the dark night.

"I have dozens of bags," Luz said.

"And I have dozens of candles," her mother said.

"And I feel strong enough to help you put sand in the bags and help you light them," abuelo said.

They laughed and hugged each other.

"Tomorrow I will tell Reina," Luz said. "She can help."

That night before she went to bed, Luz looked out the window. The little farolito she had made was still burning brightly. Tomorrow night was Christmas Eve. There would be a hundred farolitos lighting the way. Luz prayed her father would be home in time to share the joy.

The following morning Luz jumped out of bed before the sun rose. She hurried to help her abuelo light the wood stove to warm the house.

"You look happy, little one," her abuelo said.

"I am happy," Luz answered. "I can hardly wait to tell Reina the secret. And you, abuelo, how do you feel?"

Her grandfather smiled. "I feel much stronger. I think it was the oshá tea you fixed for me. I'm ready to help fill the bags with sand."

Luz hugged him. Then she went to help her mother fix breakfast. They ate hot *atole,* eggs and tortillas, and warm empanaditas.

After breakfast Luz put on her coat and mittens and ran to Reina's house. Full of excitement, she told Reina the secret of the farolitos. Then they hurried to Luz's house to make them.

Abuelo went to the arroyo and got the sand. Luz and Reina opened all the bags and put sand in the bottom. Then in the base of sand they placed the candle. When they finished, they put the little bags all in a line, from the door to the street.

They even put bags along the top of abuelo's adobe wall.

Some neighbors passed by while they were working. They couldn't understand what the bags were for. They laughed.

"What are you going to catch in the bags, falling stars?" they asked. The neighborhood kids gathered around and laughed at Luz and Reina and abuelo.

"Yes," Luz answered, "we are going to catch falling stars. Wait and see."

"Come tonight," abuelo told his neighbors.

"Oh, we will," the people laughed. "We want to see the falling stars."

Late in the afternoon when they were finished setting up the farolitos, they went inside to drink hot chocolate. Now all they had to do was wait till it got dark to light the candles.

Around them the people of the village of San Juan were busy preparing for Christmas. People went from

house to house to visit and take food to the elders. The church was scrubbed clean and the candles were lit. They would celebrate with a mass at midnight.

The pastores put on their costumes and prepared to perform their play. But there was a sadness in the air because everyone knew that abuelo was too sick to light the bonfires. The shepherds would sing about the newborn child in Bethlehem as the procession hurried to the church, but they would not stop at any house unless there were luminarias to guide them.

After Luz and Reina drank their chocolate, they waited at the window. They watched the sun set and the first wisps of snow begin to fall. Soon it was dark, and the soft snow was falling like white feathers.

"It's time to light the farolitos!" Luz shouted.

"It's time!" Reina repeated.

They looked at abuelo. "Yes, it's time," he smiled. Wrapped in their warmest coats, they went out to light the farolitos.

Abuelo held the matchbox. Luz and Reina carefully went from bag to bag and lit the candles. A hundred farolitos shone brightly in the night.

The children of the village came to see the beautiful sight. No one had ever seen farolitos like this before.

"Oh, how beautiful," the children said.

Then the pastores came down the street. They paused to look at the farolitos shining brightly in the dark.

"This is the place for our play," Gila, the shepherd girl, said. All the pastores agreed. The farolitos were the stars guiding them to Bethlehem.

The entire village gathered around and watched with delight the play of the pastores. Luz and Reina stood side by side, beaming with happiness. The dancing light of the farolitos shone in their eyes. Abuelo stood by them, happy as the children.

When the play of the pastores ended, all the players and neighbors were invited into the house to eat. Abuelo served the posole and the hot chile. Mother served the empanaditas and hot coffee.

"I feel well," abuelo said to his neighbors. "We told you we could catch falling stars!" he winked.

Luz smiled. All the village was talking about the farolitos.

"Next year every house will have farolitos," abuelo said.

Everyone was happy. From time to time they went to the window to look outside. The farolitos were glowing brightly in the dark. Around them the snow fell softly, creating a scene of peace and beauty.

When the people began to sing the songs of Christmas, Luz put on her coat and went outside alone. She was happy that her abuelo was better and that the pastores had come to their house. But she was also sad because her father had not been able to come home for Christmas.

She walked up the path to the street. Around her the farolitos glowed brightly. The snow fell softly.

What a beautiful Christmas, Luz thought. If only father was here to share it with us.

She paused as she saw a dark figure coming down the street. The figure came closer.

"Luz!" the figure called.

It was her father, and he carried a Christmas tree.

"*¡Papá!*" Luz called and ran to greet him. He swept her up in his arms.

"I'm so happy you're home," she cried and hugged him.

"It was a long trip," he said. "And I stopped to cut a Christmas tree for you. But what's this?"

He looked at the farolitos.

"We made them today. Because abuelo couldn't make the luminarias. We call them farolitos."

"They're beautiful," her father said. "I could see them from far away. A more beautiful sight I have never seen."

Then together they went into the house. Mother cried because she was happy. Father told how he came in the bus and how he saw the farolitos when he got to the village. Everyone was happy that he had returned in time for Christmas.

Abuelo set up the Christmas tree and Luz and Reina decorated it with bright yarn and popcorn strings. Father had brought a star, which they put at the top. Mother put her *nacimiento* at the bottom of the tree. The nacimiento was the small figures of Jesus in his cradle, Mary and Joseph, and the shepherds and their animals.

Then it was time for the procession to continue on to the church. Everybody went out, shouting, "*Feliz Navidad.* Merry Christmas."

That night when Luz and her family returned from church, the farolitos were still glowing brightly. In the snow they shone like guiding lights, welcoming them home.

"Farolitos de Luz," her abuelo said. "A tradition that will last for every Christmas, as long as there is love in our hearts."

TRADITIONS YOU SHARE

The tradition of the luminarias was very important to Luz and her grandfather. Write a short story about a holiday tradition in your family. Before you begin your story, think about what you want to write. What holiday does the tradition celebrate? How do you celebrate it? Which of your relatives joins in the celebration? When you have finished, share the story of your tradition with a friend.

BYRD BAYLOR

Born in San Antonio, Texas, Byrd Baylor knows the Southwest well. She lives in the southern Arizona desert in an adobe house that she built with her friends. She says of the Southwest, "Maybe everybody has a small part of the world where they feel most at home. The southwestern desert is like that for me."

One day Baylor stopped in the village of Topawa in Arizona. Someone had told her that schoolchildren from the Papago tribe were writing down Native American legends they had heard from older tribe members. Baylor loved the stories she read. She wanted to put them in a book for other people to share. So she traveled around Arizona asking other Native American children of the Southwest tribes — Navajo, Hopi, Papago, Pima, Apache, Quechan, Cocopah children — to pick stories told to them by members of their own tribes. Some children wrote the legends down. Others illustrated the stories. Finally, Baylor gathered the children's work into a book called *And It Is Still That Way.* The stories you are about to read are from this book.

FACING PAGE: *PETROGLYPH FIGURES* BY JOE HERRERA (COCHITI)

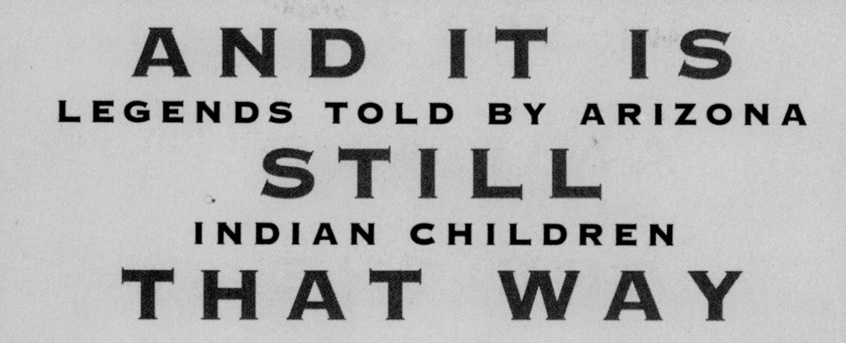

COMPILED BY

BYRD BAYLOR

WHY ANIMALS ARE THE WAY THEY ARE

POTTERY DESIGN BY JULIAN MARTINEZ (SAN ILDEFONSO)

WHY DOGS DON'T TALK ANYMORE

Old Quechan people have a favorite story that they tell to Quechan children.

They say dogs used to talk just like people. They spoke in Indian language and said anything they wanted.

Dogs lived among their Indian masters and talked all the time. The only trouble was that the dogs talked too much. They never stopped. Whenever anything happened — they told it. Whatever they heard — they told it. Whatever they saw — they told it.

No one could keep a secret. No one could hide anything. The dogs told everything. It was terrible.

The Indians got together and asked the Great Spirit: "O Great Spirit, hear our prayer. Do something about these dogs of ours. We cannot keep a secret anymore."

But the dogs went on telling this and that. Each night the people went to bed wondering what new secrets the dogs would be telling when they woke up.

One morning an old man stood up and shoved his dog.

"Well, dog," he said, "go tell everybody I shoved you."

The dog just looked at him for a minute. He said nothing.

The old man was surprised. He tried something else. He whispered a secret.

Then he said, "Well, dog, go ahead and tell everybody my secret."

Again, the dog just looked at him. He didn't say a word. He didn't tell the secret.

Instead, he BARKED. He only barked.

What a relief! The Indian people knew that the Great Spirit had found a way to answer their prayers.

When they tell it now, Quechan Indians always say that it is true dogs could once talk. But they didn't use their talking for a good cause. That's why it was taken away from them.

Now dogs bark a lot. Whenever they see a person coming into an Indian village they bark. When they hear a sound at night they bark. They always bark — but they don't tell secrets anymore.

So you better be careful how you use your talking. You might end up just having to bark.

Group story:
Kenneth Andrews, Reginald Antone, Allyson Collins, Anson Collins, Juan Davis, Wendy Davis, Ricardo Juan, Robin Juan, Ronald Juan
Quechan
Ft. Yuma Library

WHY BEARS HAVE SHORT TAILS

Fox was fishing in the river. When he had ten fish he put them on his back and walked off into the woods.

Bear came along and saw Fox with the fish on his back.

"How come you have so many fishes on your back? How are you fishing those fishes out of the water?"

Fox said, "It's easy. You sit on the ice and put your tail in the river. The fishes catch onto your tail and when you get up there will be all of those fishes just hanging on."

"Thanks," said Bear as he ran off toward the river.

He didn't know Fox was laughing as he went along through the woods with his ten fish.

Bear sat on the ice. He sat there a long time, waiting and waiting. He didn't notice any fish jumping onto his tail. All he noticed was that his tail was freezing. It hurt.

After a long time, Bear said, "I can't feel my tail."

He got up and looked. It was true. His long tail had frozen off. All he had left was a very short tail.

Bear was angry. He gave up fishing and ran into the woods looking for Fox.

Fox was cooking his ten fish when Bear grabbed him.

Bear said, "You tricked me and my beautiful long tail froze off. So now I'm taking you back to that river. I'll throw you in and let you freeze."

"No," Fox said. "Don't do that. If you let me go I'll give you all my fish."

So Bear let Fox go and ate all the fish himself and warmed his short tail by Fox's fire.

Now all bears have short tails. That is how it happened.

Sandra Begay, Navajo, Tuba City Boarding School

WHY OUR WORLD IS LIKE IT IS

Petroglyphs BY MICHAEL KABOTIE (HOPI), 1967

HOW THE PAPAGOS GOT SOME SHADE

Rattlesnake was a powerful medicine man. But even so he became very sick. His wife did everything she could for him but Rattlesnake did not get any better. He was dying.

He called his best friends, Jackrabbit, Turtle, and Coyote.

He told them, "Make me a place where I can lie until I die. I will lie on the west side in the morning and on the east side in the afternoon."

That is what he said.

His friends didn't know what kind of place he wanted. So they just dug a hole. That seemed like a good house to them.

Then they went to take Rattlesnake to his new house. Rattlesnake was disappointed but he did not let his friends know it.

He said, "It is a nice hole and you can put me in it when I die. But now make me a house like I told you."

His friends thought Rattlesnake did not know what he was saying because he was so sick. So they put up a windbreak.

But Rattlesnake did not want a windbreak. He wanted a place that would be open but would have shade on the west side in the morning and shade on the east side in the afternoon.

When Rattlesnake saw the windbreak he said, "This kind of house is good to stop the wind but it is not what I want."

What he wanted was a brush shelter. In Papago language today we call it *watto* or *ramada,* but in those days there was not a brush shelter anywhere around. No one had ever thought of building anything that way. So Rattlesnake's friends did not understand what he wanted. They quickly put up a real house.

"It's a nice house for my wife to live in after I die but it is not what I want now."

Jackrabbit and Turtle and Coyote couldn't figure out what their friend wanted.

Finally Rattlesnake told them, "Make me one that is covered like a house. The roof can be made with brush and there should be four posts to hold it up, but there should not be any walls. When the shade moves, I'll move with it."

His friends then knew what he wanted. They built the first watto and Rattlesnake died in its shade.

They buried him in the hole they had dug.

His wife moved into the house near the windbreak.

And all the Papago people use wattos for shade to this day.

Group story: Papago, Topawa School

WHY SAGUAROS GROW ON THE SOUTH SIDE OF HILLS

The world had just been made. Coyote was supposed to be helping Elder Brother plant seeds and he was walking around the empty desert with his paw closed.

Another coyote came up to him and said, "Open your hand, brother. I want to see what you have there."

He opened his hand. It was full of seeds for saguaro cactus. The other coyote hit his hand and the seeds were scattered right where they were — on the south side of a hill.

That is why even now you see saguaros growing mostly on the south side of hills. The seeds remember where Coyote threw them.

Robert Juan
Pima-Papago
Ft. Yuma Library

GREAT TROUBLES AND GREAT HEROES

RECURRENCE OF SPIRITUAL ELEMENTS BY HELEN HARDIN (SANTA CLARA), 1973

THE BRAVE MOUSE

Long ago at Old Oraibi there was a chicken hawk that killed almost all the chickens in the village. He was eating them one by one. Finally there were almost no chickens left.

Nobody in the village could kill that hawk. They talked about it down in the *kiva* where a little mouse happened to be listening. He heard the bad news.

This mouse wanted to help the people of his village. He made a plan.

First he cut a hole in the top of the kiva. Then he whittled a very sharp point on one end of a stick. He put that stick through the hole. Next, he went outside himself and sat on top of the kiva very close to the sharp stick.

He knew the hawk would see a tiny mouse and come diving down from the sky to get him. Even though he was afraid, the mouse sat there waiting.

Finally the hawk saw the mouse and came flying toward him. The mouse did not move until the hawk was almost on him. Then he jumped away and the hawk flew into the sharp stick and was killed.

The people were so happy everybody brought the mouse something good to eat.

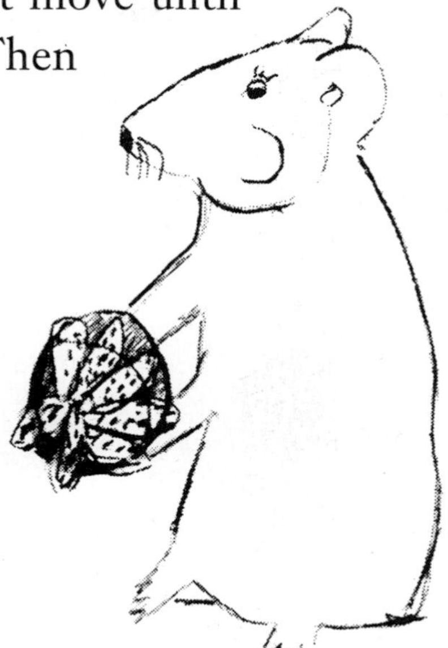

Donita Lomatska
Hopi
Phoenix Indian School

HOW THE YEI SAVED THE PEOPLE

On Navajo land you can still see a place where ancient animals and snakes were once killed by the giants called Yei.

At the beginning of the world one Yei carried a large clay pot with a great cruel snake in it. Once he stumbled and fell and the pot broke. The great snake got free. He would have killed everyone but the giant Yei fought a battle with that snake and killed it. The world was saved.

You can see where it happened. The earth looks torn up and strange rocks look like the hardened blood of a serpent.

Darlene Keams
Navajo
Tuba City Boarding School

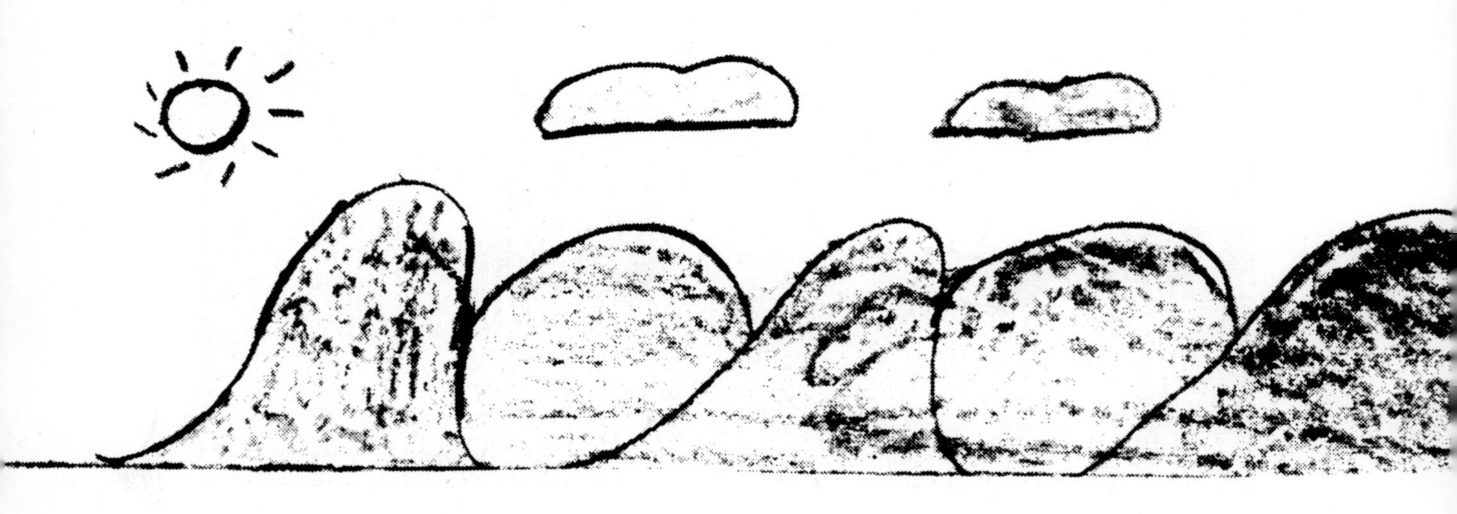

PEOPLE CAN TURN INTO ANYTHING

Enchanted Forest by Pop Chalee (Taos)

DO YOU WANT TO TURN INTO A RABBIT?

There was a boy who was so bad. He was always fussing. He said mean things to his mother, to his father, to his sister too. He was the worst person anywhere around.

This is what happened to him. They said, "You better go live by yourself."

He went out. He thought he'd find another place to live. And as he went out there in the desert he began to change. First he felt his ears getting longer . . . a lot longer. He felt his legs getting shorter . . . a lot shorter.

He was turning into a rabbit.

If you can't get along in a house, sometimes you turn into a rabbit. Then you live in a rabbit hole by yourself.

This boy decided to get along.

Reginald Antone, Quechan, Ft. Yuma Library

SEVEN PIMA STARS

This happened long ago at the place we call Homathee.

Seven Pima boys wanted to dance with the men in a ceremony that lasted all night. They knew children were not supposed to dance that ceremony but they didn't care. They started dancing around the fire just like the men.

The chief saw them. He told them, "Stop that. Something bad can happen if you dance when you are not allowed to."

The boys didn't listen to him. They went into the desert and built their own fire and danced around it all night long.

Suddenly ropes dropped down from the sky and caught the seven boys. Even then, they kept on dancing.

The boys were lifted into the air, dancing as they went.

They were lifted so high into the sky they turned into stars. You can see them there at night. If you look up you can count seven stars close together, dancing still.

Donald Sabori, Pima, St. John's School

THE EAGLE AND THE BOY

This happened long ago in the village of Old Oraibi.

People had eagles tied up on the roofs of their houses the same way we do now because eagles are important for ceremonies.

Just as it is now, somebody had to go up there every day to take care of the eagle and give it food and water.

So this boy long ago had to go up on the roof every morning before he went to work in the fields. He went up again in the evening before supper. He was the one who took care of the eagle.

The boy was busy with the work he had to do out in the cornfield. He was busy working with the squash and melons and beans but he took time when he fed the eagle to stay and talk to him. He always stayed up there on the roof as long as he could. Sometimes he even stayed up there after it was dark. As the summer passed, he told that eagle all his thoughts.

When he was not with the eagle he still thought about him. When he was eating supper with his family, he was very quiet. He would just sit there thinking about his eagle.

He got up when it was still dark so he could be with the eagle before he had to go to the fields, and out there working all day, he still thought of him.

Then one day instead of going to the fields when he was supposed to, he went back up to the eagle on the roof.

This is what he told the eagle: "I want to go with you to the place where eagles go when they die."

The boy untied his eagle and got on his back. They flew up into the sky above the village.

When they were flying over the cornfield where the boy's mother and father were working, the boy began to sing. It sounded like an eagle singing.

The people heard his song and looked up. They saw an eagle circling, moving higher and higher and higher until it was out of sight.

The mother and father sadly went home.

On the other side of the sky the eagle and the boy came to another world.

Alvin Kooyahoema
Hopi
Hotevilla-Bacabe Community School

BROTHER COYOTE

THE ORATOR BY FRED BEAVER (CREEK), 1973

COYOTE HAS TO HAVE HIS WAY

Coyote met a bumblebee. Bumblebee had something in his hand.

Coyote asked him, "What do you have there, old man?"

Bumblebee said, "I don't want anybody to meddle with this."

Coyote begged Bumblebee but Bumblebee kept saying, "This is not for you."

Coyote just *had* to know. "Please tell me, good friend."

Finally Bumblebee said, "Well, all right. But you cannot see it here. You must take it home and get your family to build you a new hut and cover the hut with skins so nothing can get in or out. Do not even have an opening at the top. Then get inside and close the door and tell your family to pile rocks up all around the outside so that you cannot get out. And then open the package."

"Oh, thank you, thank you . . ." Coyote grabbed the package and ran all the way home. He did everything Bumblebee had said.

When he was finally inside the new hut he opened the package.

Many bumblebees flew out as soon as it was opened. They stung Coyote though he yelled for help as loud as he could. Poor Coyote.

Tina Naiche
San Carlos Apache, Rice School

THE BEAUTIFUL DREAM

Many centuries ago Maii, the Coyote, was hanging around.

Coyote always liked to plan something tricky so this day he went walking with Porcupine and Brother Skunk. He was thinking as he walked along.

Ahead of them a wagon was going down the road. They saw a piece of meat fall off. They all ran for it and they all got there about the same time.

But Coyote did not want to share the meat so he said, "That's not fair."

He suggested they all race down a hill and the winner would eat the meat by himself. So that is what they did.

The race started. Porcupine curled up and rolled down the hill. He won.

"That's not fair," Coyote said.

Coyote suggested another plan. He said, "The one who dreams the most beautiful dream will eat that meat."

So that is what they planned.

Coyote and Skunk went to sleep but Porcupine stayed awake. He had a plan of his own.

Finally Coyote and Skunk woke up and told their dreams. They were both good dreams. They were both beautiful dreams.

Then they asked Porcupine what he had dreamed.

Porcupine said, "I dreamed I ate the meat."

They all jumped up and looked in the tree where they had left the meat. The meat was gone and Porcupine was looking fat.

Lana Semallie, Navajo, Tuba City Boarding School

THERE IS MAGIC ALL AROUND US

CHANGEABLE WOLF MAN BY HA SO DE (NAVAJO), 1958

HOPI KACHINAS

Kachinas
look so beautiful
dance so well
sing songs no one else can sing.
Their songs make
everyone feel good.
If you were Hopi you'd be proud.

Winifred Secakuku
Hopi
Second Mesa Day School

ONE WHO HAD THE POWER OF OWLS

There used to be a woman who understood everything the owl said with his strange cries. She used to go outside every time the owls came and hooted for her. Sometimes they told her who was going to die in the village.

This woman had the power of owls. Once people thought she was going to die, but she told them that even though she might seem to be dead she would not be. She told them to wait four days before they had any ceremonies for her. She lay dead for three days but on

the fourth day she came to life again and went on talking to owls.

After that she was a medicine woman, a doctor. She used owl feathers to heal the sick. Once some men wanted to steal her power so they stole her owl feathers from her medicine bundle and buried them by a small post.

The gray owl came to her and told her in his owl language where the feathers were and who had taken them. She understood him and went and dug her feathers up.

No one could fool that woman and after that no one tried to. They knew she had the power of owls.

Francine Redbird
Pima
St. John's School

APACHES LIVE CLOSE TO NATURE

The Apache tribe began from the two sons of Changing Woman. The father of one of those sons was WATER and the father of the other was SUN.

Since that time everything in nature has been sacred to Apaches. We are related to water and to sun.

There is a mountain in San Carlos which is held in higher regard than any other mountain. It is called Triplets.

We are told not to climb up there and disturb anything because if a little child were to touch something there he would not grow up but would stay a child forever.

Apaches believe the balance of nature should be kept and all parts held in reverence.

Group story: San Carlos Apache, Rice School

WE ARE KIN TO TREES

The Great Star Man went to chop down a tree to make a shelter for his people. But before he put the axe to the tree, the tree fell down beside him.

The tree said, "Do not chop me. I am your father. You are my son."

That happened at the beginning of the world. It has happened since. Someone — always an Indian — will go to chop a tree and that tree will speak aloud and say, "Do not chop me. I am your father. You are my son."

It is true.

It is still that way.

Carla Soke and Karen Chiago
Pima
St. John's School

PASS IT ON

The stories you have just read were written down by Native American children as they remembered hearing them told. What stories have been passed on in your family? With a partner or in a small group, share stories, songs, or rhymes someone in your family has told to you or read to you.

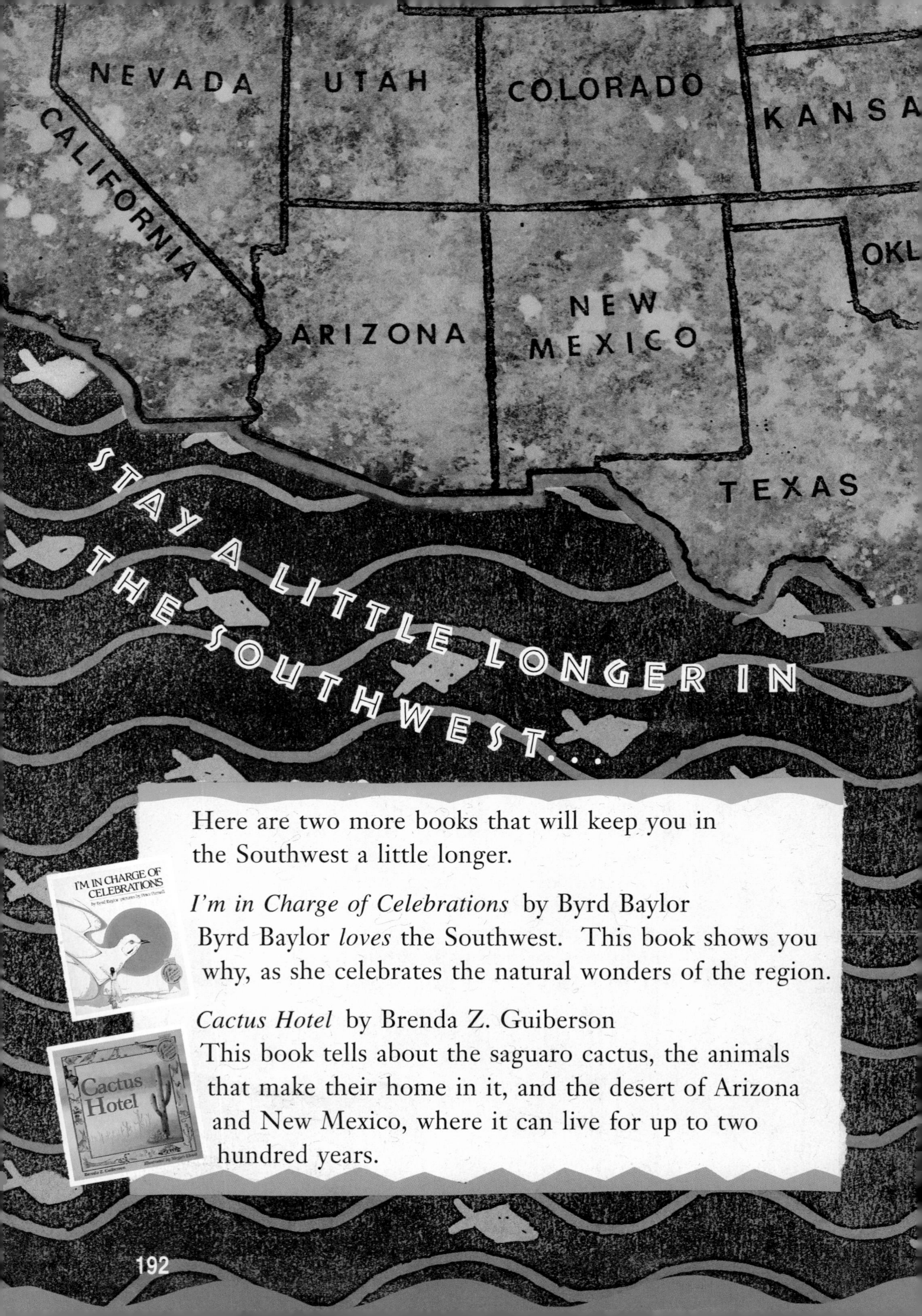

STAY A LITTLE LONGER IN THE SOUTHWEST...

Here are two more books that will keep you in the Southwest a little longer.

I'm in Charge of Celebrations by Byrd Baylor
Byrd Baylor *loves* the Southwest. This book shows you why, as she celebrates the natural wonders of the region.

Cactus Hotel by Brenda Z. Guiberson
This book tells about the saguaro cactus, the animals that make their home in it, and the desert of Arizona and New Mexico, where it can live for up to two hundred years.

. . . or Travel to Some Other Places

Here are more books, by authors from other regions in North America. Read them and share these authors' favorite places.

In Coal Country by Judith Hendershot
The author tells of many special moments she remembers growing up in a small Ohio coal-mining town.

Arctic Memories by Normee Ekoomiak
What would it be like to sleep in an iglu? What is the blanket-toss game? Normee Ekoomiak tells about his own childhood as an Inuit in northern Canada.

Aunt Flossie's Hats (and Crab Cakes Later)
by Elizabeth Fitzgerald Howard
Sarah and Susan look forward to Sunday afternoons with Aunt Flossie. With each of her old hats they try on, Aunt Flossie tells a story about growing up in Baltimore, Maryland.

From the Hills of Georgia by Mattie Lou O'Kelley
With words and paintings, Mattie Lou O'Kelley tells about growing up on a farm in Georgia in the early 1900's.

The Carp in the Bathtub by Barbara Cohen
Mama keeps a live carp in the bathtub to eat for Passover. But Leah and Harry like the fish and decide to rescue it in this story set in the Flatbush section of New York City in the early 1900's.

FANTASY

BEWARE! TROUBLE AHEAD

BEWARE OF

THE WOLF!

BEWARE OF

MICE EATERS!

BEWARE OF DOG HATERS!

THE
CHARACTERS
YOU WILL MEET IN
THIS BOOK ALL HAVE GOOD
REASON TO PAY ATTENTION
TO WARNING SIGNS. READ
THESE STORIES
TO FIND OUT
WHY.

CONTENTS

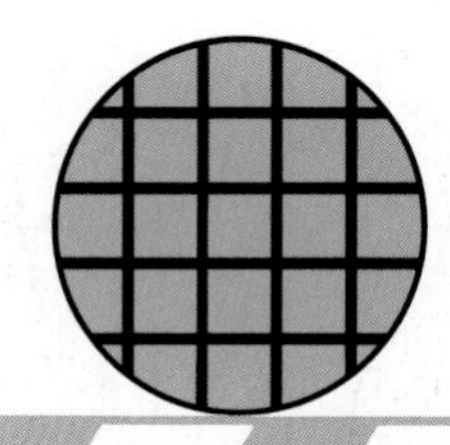

CAUTION

Doctor De Soto

story and pictures by William Steig

Doctor De Soto, the dentist, did very good work, so he had no end of patients. Those close to his own size — moles, chipmunks, et cetera — sat in the regular dentist's chair.

Larger animals sat on the floor, while Doctor De Soto stood on a ladder.

For extra-large animals, he had a special room. There Doctor De Soto was hoisted up to the patient's mouth by his assistant, who also happened to be his wife.

Doctor De Soto was especially popular with the big animals. He was able to work inside their mouths, wearing rubbers to keep his feet dry; and his fingers were so delicate, and his drill so dainty, they could hardly feel any pain.

Being a mouse, he refused to treat animals dangerous to mice, and it said so on his sign. When the doorbell rang, he and his wife would look out the window. They wouldn't admit even the most timid-looking cat.

One day, when they looked out, they saw a well-dressed fox with a flannel bandage around his jaw.

"I cannot treat you, sir!" Doctor De Soto shouted. "Sir! Haven't you read my sign?"

"Please!" the fox wailed. "Have mercy, I'm suffering!" And he wept so bitterly it was pitiful to see.

"Just a moment," said Doctor De Soto. "That poor fox," he whispered to his wife. "What shall we do?"

"Let's risk it," said Mrs. De Soto. She pressed the buzzer and let the fox in.

He was up the stairs in a flash. "Bless your little hearts," he cried, falling to his knees. "I beg you, *do* something! My tooth is killing me."

"Sit on the floor, sir," said Doctor De Soto, "and remove the bandage, please."

Doctor De Soto climbed up the ladder and bravely entered the fox's mouth. "Ooo-wow!" he gasped. The fox had a rotten bicuspid and unusually bad breath.

"This tooth will have to come out," Doctor De Soto announced. "But we can make you a new one."

"Just stop the pain," whimpered the fox, wiping some tears away.

Despite his misery, he realized he had a tasty little morsel in his mouth, and his jaw began to quiver. "Keep open!" yelled Doctor De Soto. "Wide open!" yelled his wife.

"I'm giving you gas now," said Doctor De Soto. "You won't feel a thing when I yank that tooth."

Soon the fox was in dreamland. "M-m-m, yummy," he mumbled. "How I love them raw . . . with just a pinch of salt. . . ."

They could guess what he was dreaming about. Mrs. De Soto handed her husband a pole to keep the fox's mouth open.

Doctor De Soto fastened his extractor to the bad tooth. Then he and his wife began turning the winch.

Finally, with a sucking sound, the tooth popped out and hung swaying in the air.

"I'm bleeding!" the fox yelped when he came to.

Doctor De Soto ran up the ladder and stuffed some gauze in the hole. "The worst is over," he said. "I'll have your new tooth ready tomorrow. Be here at eleven sharp."

The fox, still woozy, said goodbye and left. On his way home, he wondered if it would be shabby of him to eat the De Sotos when the job was done.

After office hours, Mrs. De Soto molded a tooth of pure gold and polished it. "Raw with salt, indeed," muttered Doctor De Soto. "How foolish to trust a fox!"

"He didn't know what he was saying," said Mrs. De Soto. "Why should he harm us? We're helping him."

"Because he's a fox!" said Doctor De Soto. "They're wicked, wicked creatures."

That night the De Sotos lay awake worrying. "Should we let him in tomorrow?" Mrs. De Soto wondered.

"Once I start a job," said the dentist firmly, "I finish it. My father was the same way."

"But we must do something to protect ourselves," said his wife. They talked and talked until they formed a plan. "I think it will work," said Doctor De Soto. A minute later he was snoring.

The next morning, promptly at eleven, a very cheerful fox turned up. He was feeling not a particle of pain.

When Doctor De Soto got into his mouth, he snapped it shut for a moment, then opened wide and laughed. "Just a joke!" he chortled.

"Be serious," said the dentist sharply. "We have work to do." His wife was lugging the heavy tooth up the ladder.

"Oh, I love it!" exclaimed the fox. "It's just beautiful."

Doctor De Soto set the gold tooth in its socket and hooked it up to the teeth on both sides.

The fox caressed the new tooth with his tongue. "My, it feels good," he thought. "I really shouldn't eat them. On the other hand, how can I resist?"

"We're not finished," said Doctor De Soto, holding up a large jug. "I have here a remarkable preparation developed only recently by my wife and me. With just one application, you can be rid of toothaches forever. How would you like to be the first one to receive this unique treatment?"

"I certainly would!" the fox declared. "I'd be honored." He hated any kind of personal pain.

"You will never have to see us again," said Doctor De Soto.

"*No one* will see you again," said the fox to himself. He had definitely made up his mind to eat them — with the help of his brand-new tooth.

Doctor De Soto stepped into the fox's mouth with a bucket of secret formula and proceeded to paint each tooth. He hummed as he worked. Mrs. De Soto stood by on the ladder, pointing out spots he had missed. The fox looked very happy.

When the dentist was done, he stepped out. "Now close your jaws tight," he said, "and keep them closed for a full minute." The fox did as he was told. Then he tried to open his mouth — but his teeth were stuck together!

"Ah, excuse me, I should have mentioned," said Doctor De Soto, "you won't be able to open your mouth for a day or two. The secret formula must first permeate the dentine. But don't worry. No pain ever again!"

The fox was stunned. He stared at Doctor De Soto, then at his wife. They smiled, and waited. All he could do was say, "Frank oo berry mush" through his clenched teeth, and get up and leave. He tried to do so with dignity.

Then he stumbled down the stairs in a daze.

Doctor De Soto and his assistant had outfoxed the fox. They kissed each other and took the rest of the day off.

Dangerous Patients

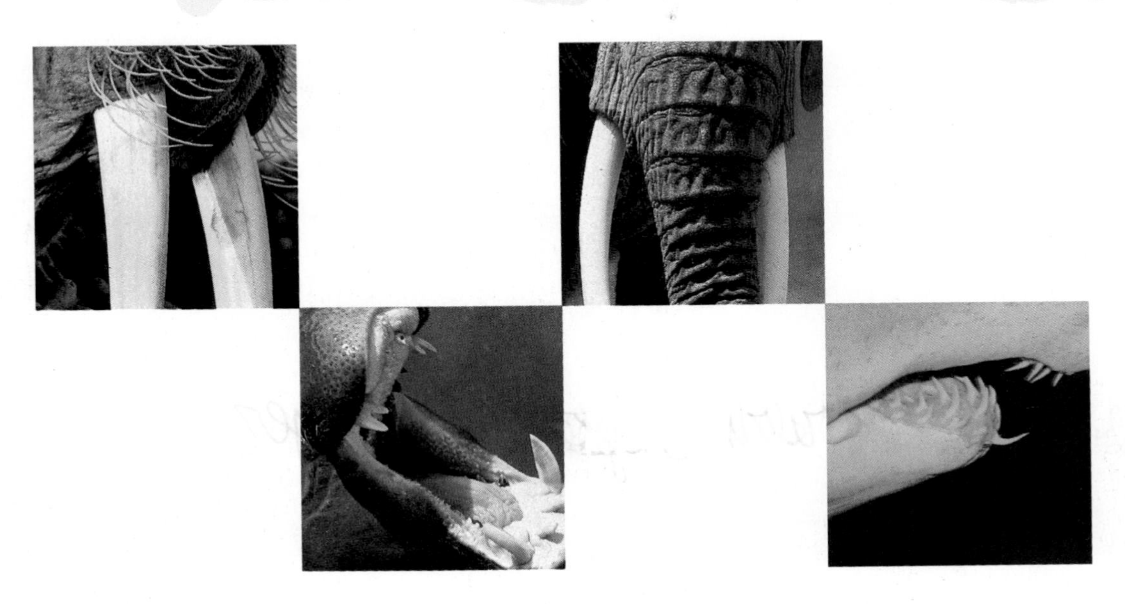

Most dentists keep records of all of their patients. Write a report about Doctor De Soto's most dangerous patient yet, the fox. Include in the report the patient's problems, behavior, and any other unusual facts. Be sure to suggest your ideas for the best treatment for the fox.

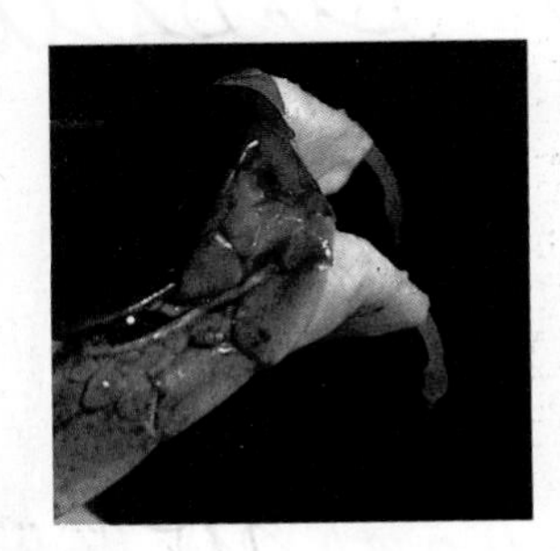

Lon Po Po
A RED-RIDING HOOD STORY FROM CHINA
TRANSLATED AND ILLUSTRATED BY
ED YOUNG

Once, long ago, there was a woman who lived alone in the country with her three children, Shang, Tao, and Paotze. On the day of their grandmother's birthday, the good mother set off to see her, leaving the three children at home.

Before she left, she said, "Be good while I am away, my heart-loving children; I will not return tonight. Remember to close the door tight at sunset and latch it well."

But an old wolf lived nearby and saw the good mother leave. At dusk, disguised as an old woman, he came up to the house of the children and knocked on the door twice: bang, bang.

Shang, who was the eldest, said through the latched door, "Who is it?"

"My little jewels," said the wolf, "this is your grandmother, your Po Po."

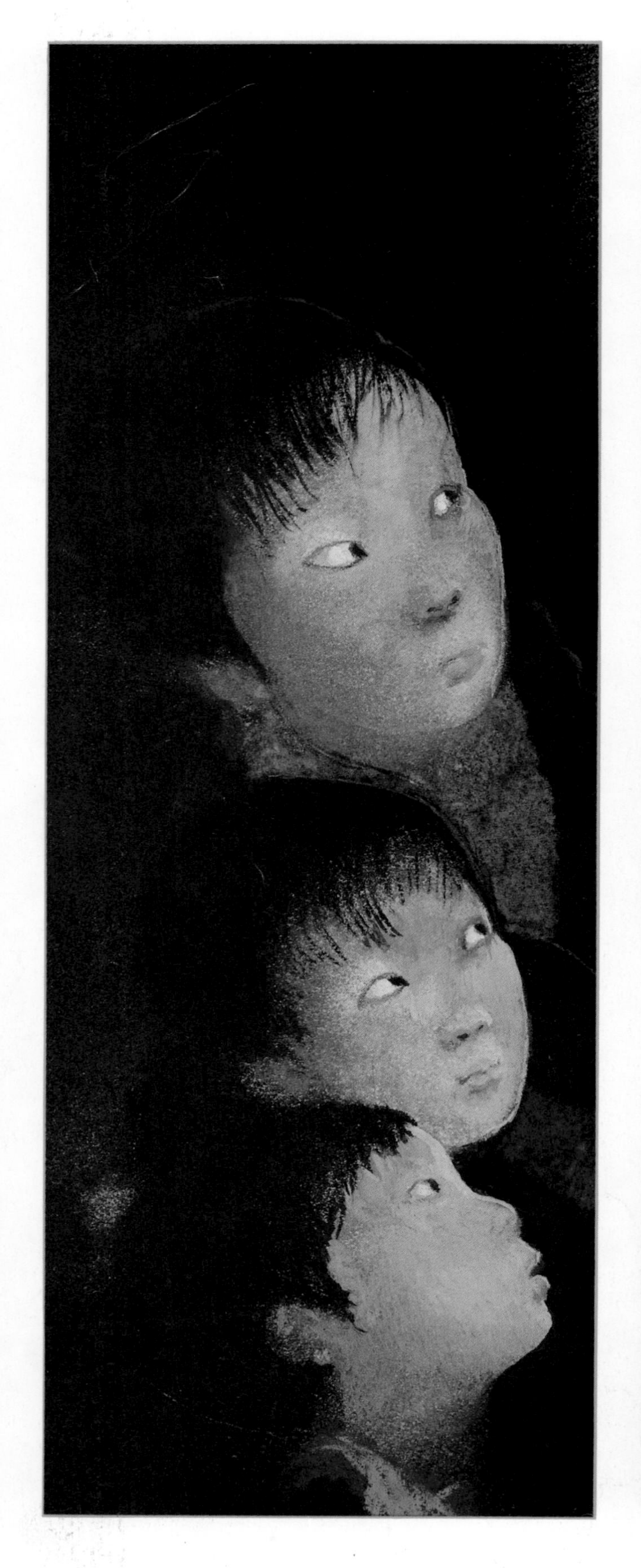

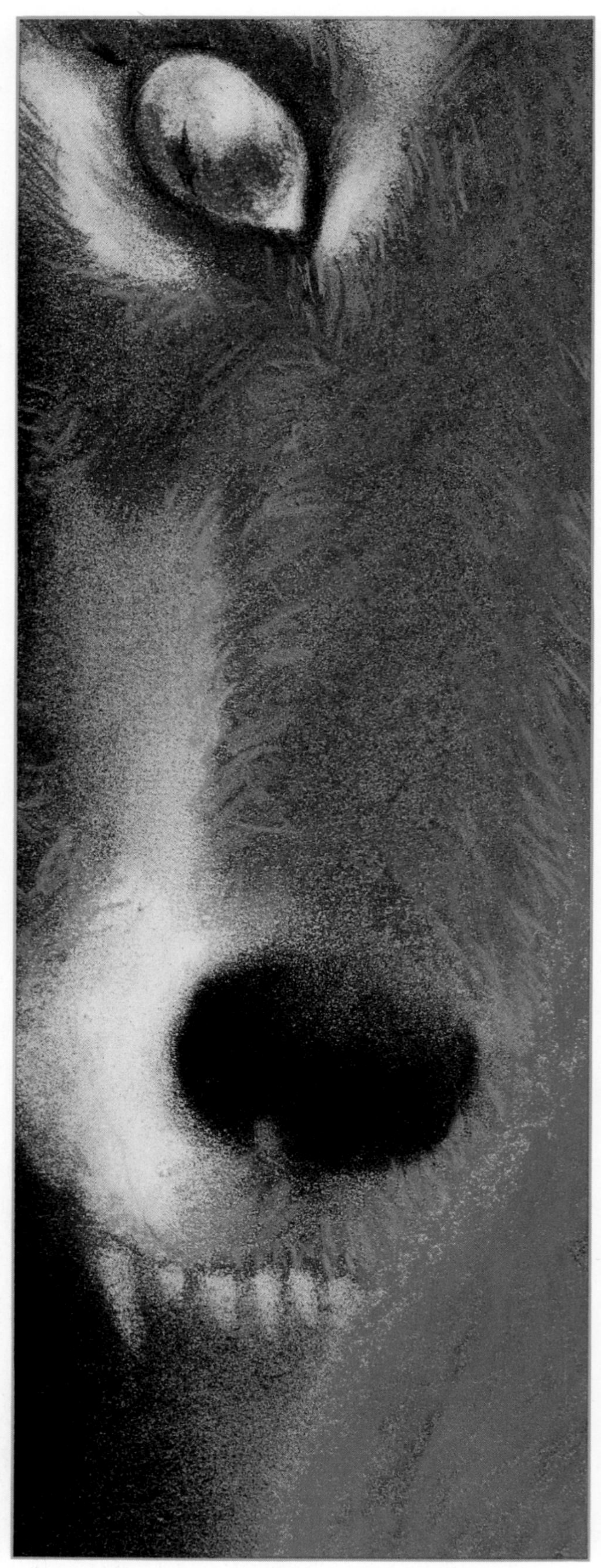

"Po Po!" Shang said. "Our mother has gone to visit you!"

The wolf acted surprised. "To visit me? I have not met her along the way. She must have taken a different route."

"Po Po!" Shang said. "How is it that you come so late?"

The wolf answered, "The journey is long, my children, and the day is short."

Shang listened through the door. "Po Po," she said, "why is your voice so low?"

"Your grandmother has caught a cold, good children, and it is dark and windy out here. Quickly open up, and let your Po Po come in," the cunning wolf said.

Tao and Paotze could not wait. One unlatched the door and the other opened it. They shouted, "Po Po, Po Po, come in!"

At the moment he entered the door, the wolf blew out the candle.

"Po Po," Shang asked, "why did you blow out the candle? The room is now dark."

The wolf did not answer.

Tao and Paotze rushed to their Po Po and wished to be hugged. The old wolf held Tao. "Good child, you are so plump." He embraced Paotze. "Good child, you have grown to be so sweet."

Soon the old wolf pretended to be sleepy. He yawned. "All the chicks are in the coop," he said. "Po Po is sleepy too." When he climbed into the big bed, Paotze climbed in at one end with the wolf, and Shang and Tao climbed in at the other.

But when Shang stretched, she touched the wolf's tail. "Po Po, Po Po, your foot has a bush on it."

"Po Po has brought hemp strings to weave you a basket," the wolf said.

Shang touched grandmother's sharp claws. "Po Po, Po Po, your hand has thorns on it."

"Po Po has brought an awl to make shoes for you," the wolf said.

At once, Shang lit the light and the wolf blew it out again, but Shang had seen the wolf's hairy face.

"Po Po, Po Po," she said, for she was not only the eldest, she was the most clever, "you must be hungry. Have you eaten gingko nuts?"

"What is gingko?" the wolf asked.

"Gingko is soft and tender, like the skin of a baby. One taste and you will live forever," Shang said, "and the nuts grow on the top of the tree just outside the door."

The wolf gave a sigh. "Oh, dear. Po Po is old,

her bones have become brittle. No longer can she climb trees."

"Good Po Po, we can pick some for you," Shang said.

The wolf was delighted.

Shang jumped out of bed and Tao and Paotze came with her to the gingko tree. There, Shang told her sisters about the wolf and all three climbed up the tall tree.

The wolf waited and waited. Plump Tao did not come back. Sweet Paotze did not come back. Shang did not come back, and no one brought any nuts from the gingko tree. At last the wolf shouted, "Where are you, children?"

"Po Po," Shang called out, "we are on the top of the tree eating gingko nuts."

"Good children," the wolf begged, "pluck some for me."

"But Po Po, gingko is magic only when it is

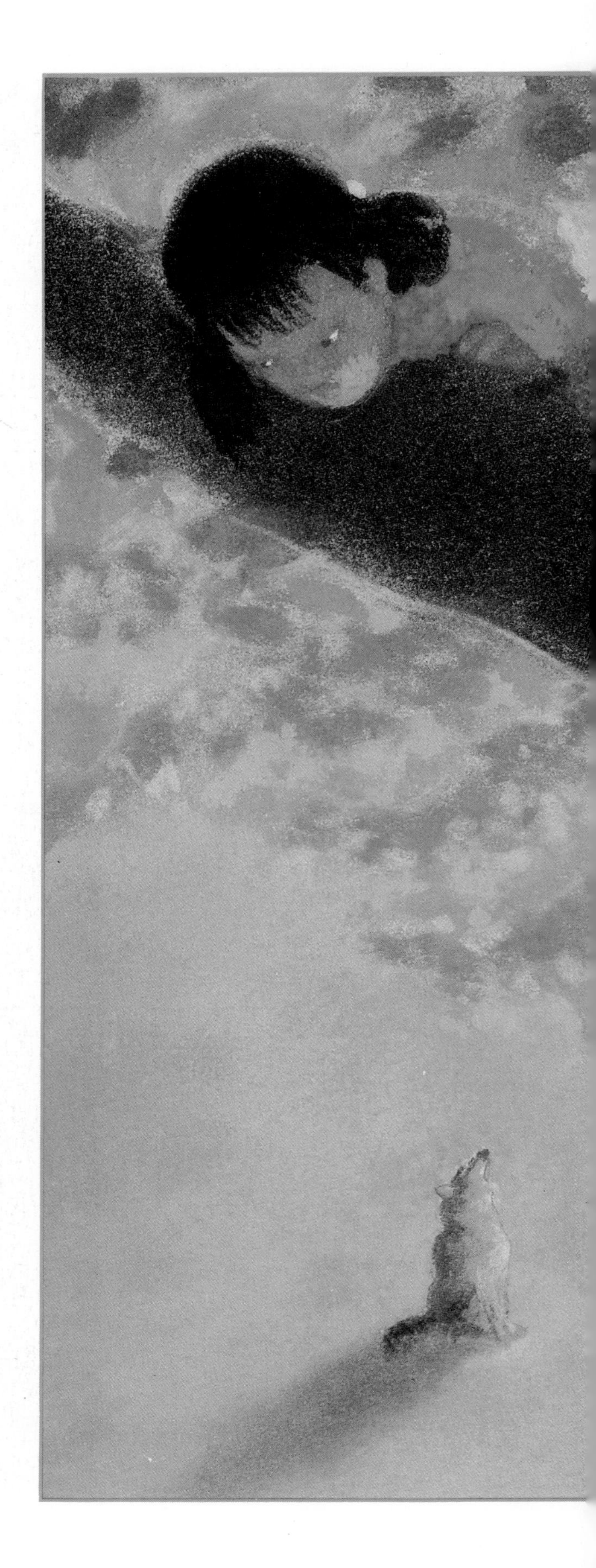

plucked directly from the tree. You must come and pluck it from the tree yourself."

The wolf came outside and paced back and forth under the tree where he heard the three children eating the gingko nuts at the top. "Oh, Po Po, these nuts are so tasty! The skin so tender," Shang said. The wolf's mouth began to water for a taste.

Finally, Shang, the eldest and most clever child, said, "Po Po, Po Po, I have a plan. At the door there is a big basket. Behind it is a rope. Tie the rope to the basket, sit in the basket and throw the other end to me. I can pull you up."

The wolf was overjoyed and fetched the basket and the rope, then threw one end of the rope to the top of the tree. Shang caught the rope and began to pull the basket up and up.

Halfway she let go of the rope, and the basket and the wolf fell to the ground.

"I am so small and weak, Po Po," Shang pretended. "I could not hold the rope alone."

"This time I will help," Tao said. "Let us do it again."

The wolf had only one thought in his mind: to taste a gingko nut. He climbed into the basket again. Now Shang and Tao pulled the rope on the basket together, higher and higher.

Again, they let go, and again the wolf tumbled down, down, and bumped his head.

The wolf was furious. He growled and cursed. "We could not hold the rope, Po Po," Shang said, "but only one gingko nut and you will be well again."

"I shall give a hand to my sisters this time," Paotze, the youngest, said.

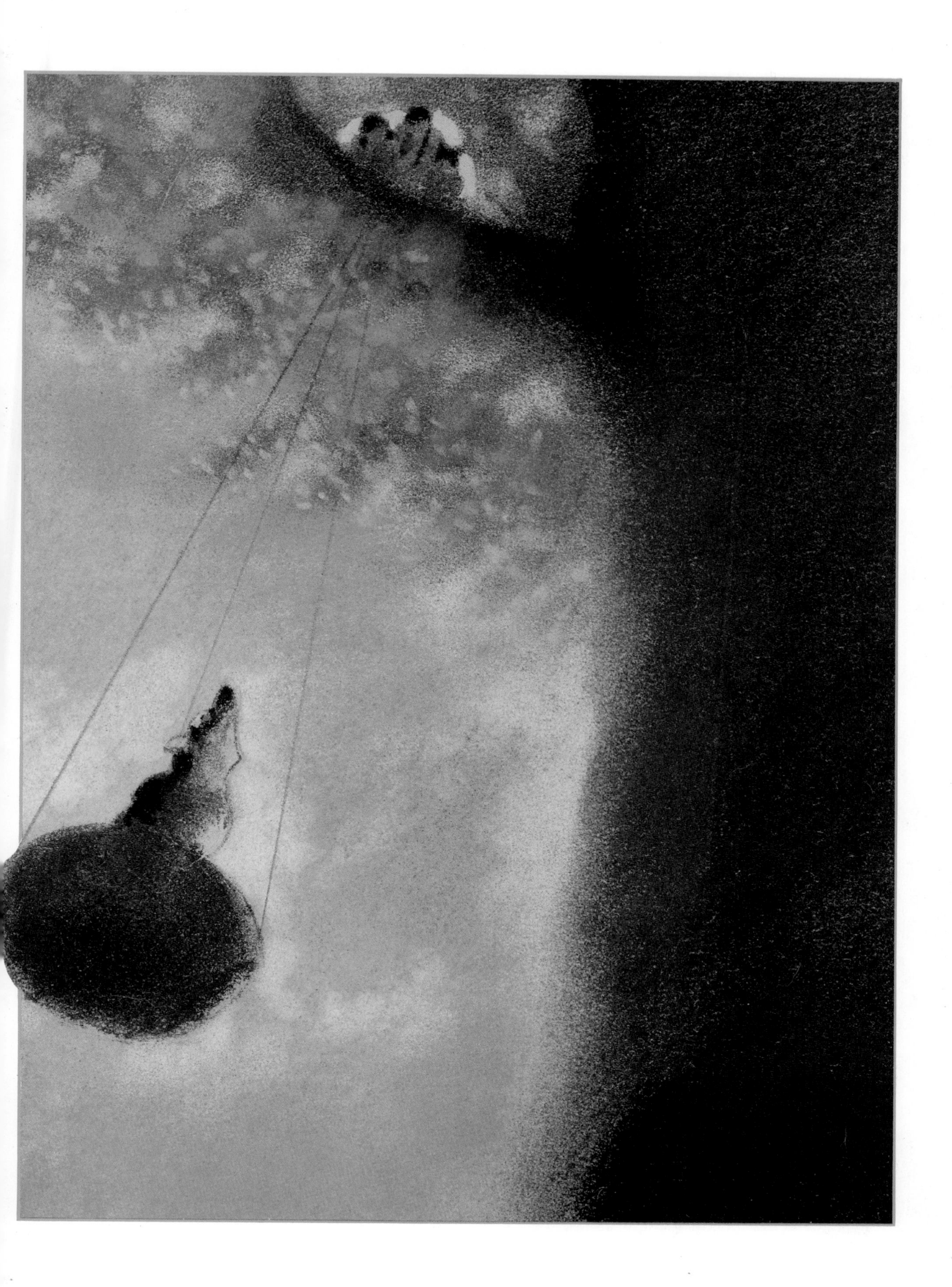

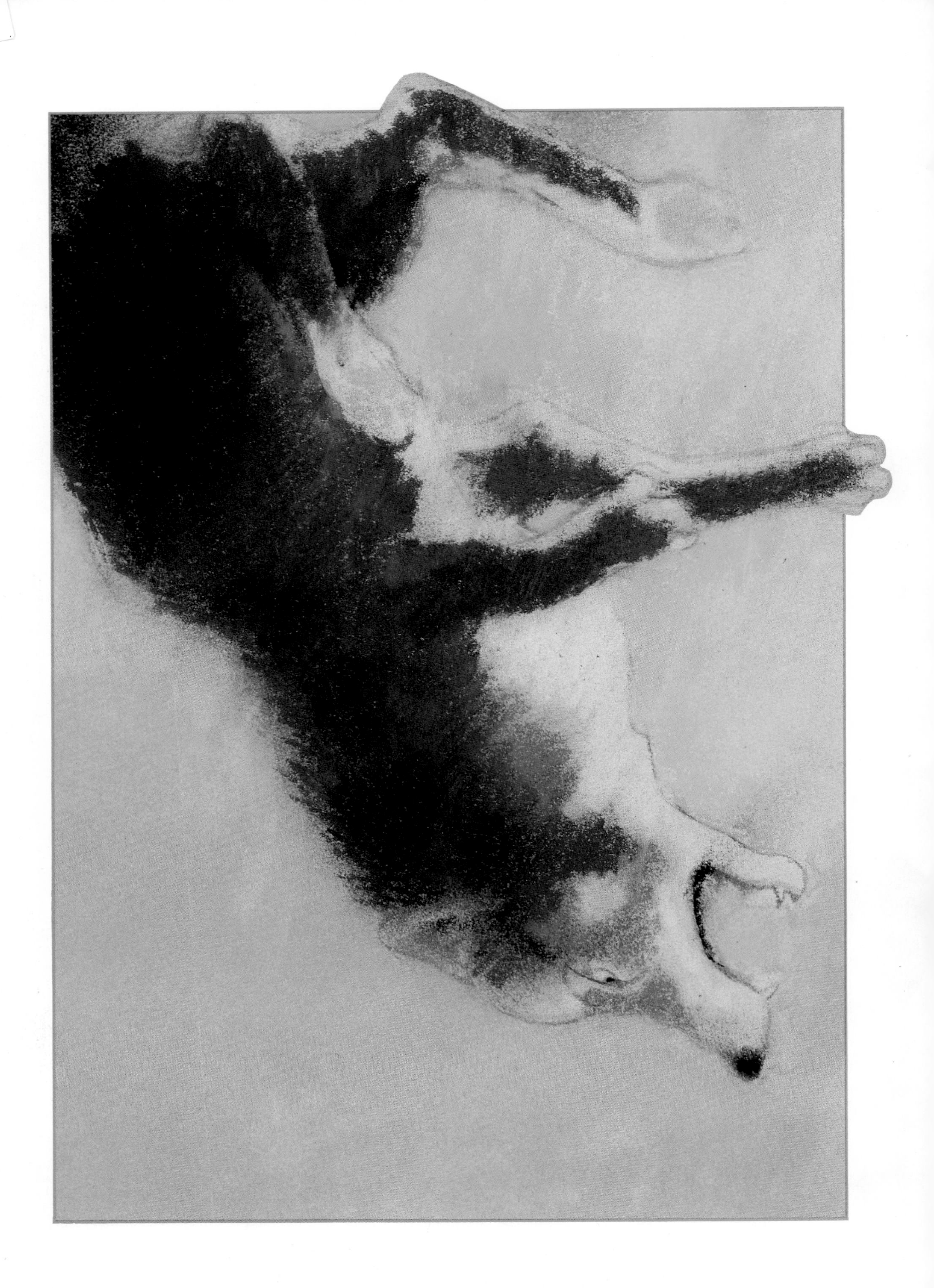

"This time we shall not fail."

Now the children pulled the rope with all of their strength. As they pulled they sang, "Hei yo, hei yo," and the basket rose straight up, higher than the first time, higher than the second time, higher and higher and higher until it nearly reached the top of the tree. When the wolf reached out, he could almost touch the highest branch.

But at that moment, Shang coughed and they all let go of the rope, and the basket fell down and down and down. Not only did the wolf bump his head, but he broke his heart to pieces.

"Po Po," Shang shouted, but there was no answer.

"Po Po," Tao shouted, but there was no answer.

"Po Po," Paotze shouted. There was still no answer. The children climbed to the branches just above the wolf and saw that he was truly dead. Then they climbed down, went into the house, closed the door, locked the door with the latch and fell peacefully asleep.

On the next day, their mother returned with baskets of food from their real Po Po, and the three sisters told her the story of the Po Po who had come.

Climb In, Grandma!

In groups of four, act out the scene from *Lon Po Po* in which Shang and her sisters try three times to get rid of the wolf. See if you can make the story come alive without using any words or objects. How will you and your group show Shang and her sisters tricking the wolf to get him in the basket? How will you show them pulling the wolf up the tree and then dropping him to the ground? When you and your group have practiced your scene, act it out for your classmates.

THE GARDEN OF ABDUL GASAZI

written and illustrated by Chris Van Allsburg

Six times Miss Hester's dog Fritz had bitten dear cousin Eunice. So when Miss Hester received an invitation to visit Eunice she was not surprised to read "P.S., Please leave your dog home." On the day of her visit Miss Hester asked young Alan Mitz to stay with Fritz and give him his afternoon walk.

As soon as Miss Hester left, Fritz ran into the parlor. He loved to chew on the chairs and shake the stuffing out of the pillows. But Alan was ready. All morning long he kept Fritz from sinking his sharp little teeth into the furniture. Finally the dog gave up and fell asleep, exhausted. Alan took a nap, too, but first he hid his hat under his shirt, hats being one of Fritz's favorite things to chew.

An hour later Alan quickly awoke when Fritz gave him a bite on the nose. The bad-mannered dog was ready for his afternoon walk. Alan fastened Fritz's leash and the dog dragged him out of the house.

Walking along, they discovered a small white bridge at the side of the road. Alan decided to let Fritz lead the way across.

Some distance beyond the bridge Alan stopped to read a sign. It said: ABSOLUTELY, POSITIVELY NO DOGS ALLOWED IN THIS GARDEN. At the bottom it was signed: ABDUL GASAZI, RETIRED MAGICIAN. Behind the sign stood a vine-covered wall with an open doorway. Alan took the warning quite seriously. He turned to leave, but as he did, Fritz gave a tremendous tug and snapped right out of his collar. He bolted straight ahead through the open door, with Alan running right behind.

"Fritz, stop, you bad dog!" cried Alan, but the dog simply ignored him.

Down shadowed paths and across sunlit lawns they

raced, deeper and deeper into the garden. Finally, Alan drew close enough to grab hold of Fritz. But as he reached out he slipped and fell. Fritz barked with laughter as he galloped out of sight. Alan slowly picked himself up. He knew he had to find Fritz before Mr. Gasazi discovered him. Bruised and tired, he hurried off in the dog's direction.

After a long search Alan was ready to give up. He was afraid he might never find Fritz. But then he came upon fresh dog prints. Slowly he followed Fritz's tracks along a path that led into a forest. The dirt path ended and a brick wall began. There were no more tracks to follow, but Alan was certain that Fritz must be just ahead.

Alan started running. In front of him he could see a clearing in the forest. As he came dashing out of the

woods he stopped as quickly as if he had run up against a wall. For there, in front of him, stood a truly awesome sight. It was the house of Gasazi. Alan nervously climbed the great stairs, convinced Fritz had come this way and been captured.

The boy's heart was pounding when he arrived at the huge door. He took a deep breath and reached for the bell, but before he touched it the door swung open. There, in the shadow of the hallway, stood Gasazi the Great. "Greetings, do come in" was all that he said.

Alan followed Gasazi into a large room. When the magician turned around Alan quickly apologized for letting Fritz into the garden. He politely asked that, if Mr. Gasazi had Fritz, would he please give him back?

The magician listened carefully and then, smiling, said, "Certainly you may have your little Fritzie. Follow me." With those words he went to the door and led Alan back outside.

They were walking across the lawn when suddenly Gasazi stopped by a gathering of ducks. He began to speak in a voice that was more like a growl. "I detest dogs. They dig up my flowers, they chew on my trees. Do you know what I do to dogs I find in my garden?"

"What?" whispered Alan, almost afraid to hear the answer.

"I TURN THEM INTO DUCKS!" bellowed Gasazi.

In horror, Alan looked at the birds in front of him. When one duck came forward, Gasazi said, "There's your Fritz."

Alan begged the magician to change Fritz

back. "Impossible," he answered, "only time can do that. This spell may last years or perhaps just a day. Now take your dear bird and please don't come again."

When Alan took the bird in his arms it tried to give him a bite. "Good old boy," said Alan sadly as he patted the bird on the head. "You really haven't changed so much." With tears in his eyes he started for home. Behind him Alan could hear Gasazi laughing. As he approached the stairway, a gust of wind took Alan's hat sailing right off his head. Running along with one arm reaching for the hat, Alan lost his hold on Fritz. The duck flew out ahead and grabbed the hat in midair. But instead of landing he just kept on flying, higher and higher, until he disappeared in the afternoon clouds.

Alan just stood and stared at the empty sky. "Goodbye, old fellow," he called out sadly, sure that Fritz was gone forever. At least he had something to chew on. Slowly, one step after another, Alan found his way back to the garden gate and over the bridge. It was sunset by the time he reached Miss Hester's. Lights were on and he knew she must be home. With a heavy heart he approached the door, wondering how Miss Hester would take the news.

When Miss Hester came to the door Alan blurted out his incredible story. He could barely hold back the tears; then, racing out of the kitchen, dog food on his nose, came Fritz. Alan couldn't believe his eyes.

"I'm afraid Mr. Gasazi played a trick on you," said Miss Hester, trying to hide a smile. "Fritz was in the

front yard when I returned. He must have found his own way home while you were with Mr. Gasazi. You see, Alan, no one can really turn dogs into ducks; that old magician just made you think that duck was Fritz."

Alan felt very silly. He promised himself he'd never be fooled like that again. He was too old to believe in magic. Miss Hester watched from the porch as Alan waved goodbye and hurried down the road to go home. Then she called out to Fritz, who was playfully running around the front yard. He came trotting up the front steps with something in his mouth and dropped it at Miss Hester's feet. "Why you bad dog," she said. "What are you doing with Alan's hat?"

HOW DID THAT HAT GET THERE?

How do you think Fritz got Alan's hat? Could Abdul Gasazi have actually changed Fritz into a duck? Think of an explanation for how the hat might have gotten into the front yard. Then discuss your explanation with your classmates. Try to convince them that your explanation is what really happened.

ALLIGATOR

If you want to see an alligator
you must go down to the muddy slushy end
of the old Caroony River

I know an alligator
who's living down there
She's a-big. She's a-mean. She's a-wild.
She's a-fierce.

But if you really want to see an alligator
you must go down to the muddy slushy end
of the old Caroony River

Go down gently to that river and say
"Alligator Mama
Alligator Mama
Alligator Mamaaaaaaaa"

And up she'll rise
but don't stick around
RUN FOR YOUR LIFE

Grace Nichols

AUTHOR-ILLUSTRATORS

Ed Young

Chris Van Allsburg

William Steig

WILLIAM STEIG

William Steig began his career as a cartoonist. He sold his first drawing in the 1930's and since then he has drawn for national magazines. When he was sixty-one years old he wrote his first children's book, *Roland the Minstrel Pig*. Steig has written and illustrated other books that you might enjoy including *Amos & Boris,* about a friendship between a mouse and a whale, and *Spinky Sulks,* about a boy who sulks all day.

from *Amos & Boris*

from *Spinky Sulks*

ED YOUNG

Ed Young was born in Tientsin, China and raised in Shanghai and Hong Kong. He came to the United States as a young man. Young translated and illustrated *Lon Po Po,* which won the Caldecott Medal in 1990. As practice for his illustrations in *Lon Po Po,* Young made a large number of drawings of real wolves. He studied how wolves move and how they communicate with each other using their ears and their tails. Young wanted to make certain that the wolf in the story looked like a real wolf. Among many books Ed Young has illustrated are *Chinese Mother Goose Rhymes* and *Foolish Rabbit's Big Mistake.*

from *Chinese Mother Goose Rhymes*

from *Foolish Rabbit's Big Mistake*

CHRIS VAN ALLSBURG

Drawing was just a hobby for Chris Van Allsburg. But a friend who liked his work suggested he try illustrating a book. So in his spare time he did pencil drawings of a little boy, a dog, and a magician. The story became *The Garden of Abdul Gasazi.* Today Chris Van Allsburg is one of the most popular author-illustrators in the history of children's literature. You might also enjoy reading his books *The Polar Express* (for which Van Allsburg won a Caldecott Medal), *Two Bad Ants,* and *Just a Dream.*

from *Just a Dream*

from *The Polar Express*

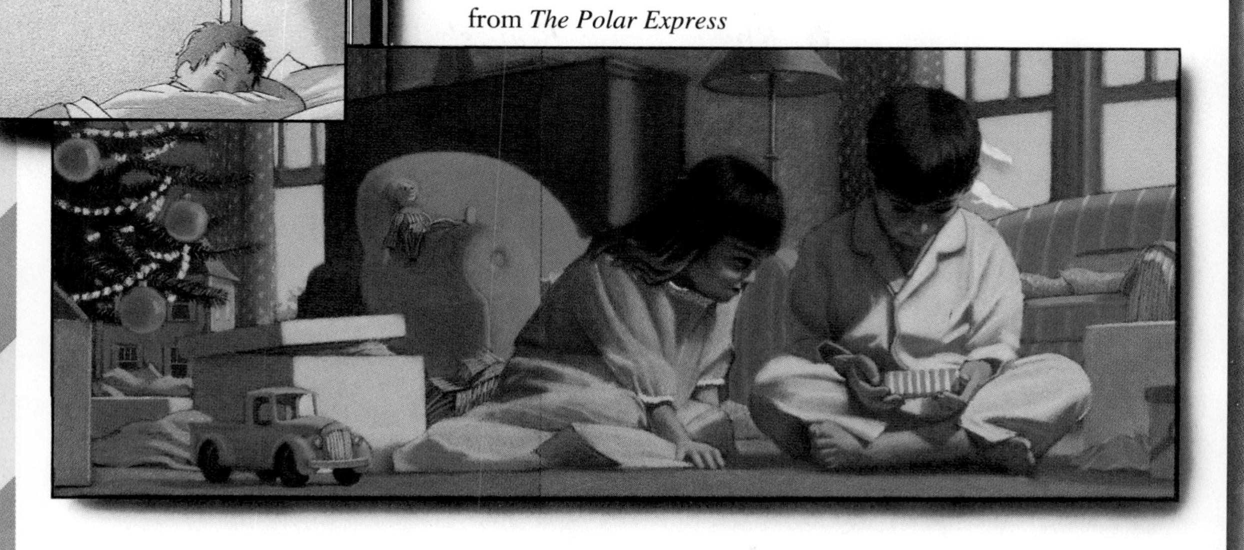

STOP FOR THESE BOOKS

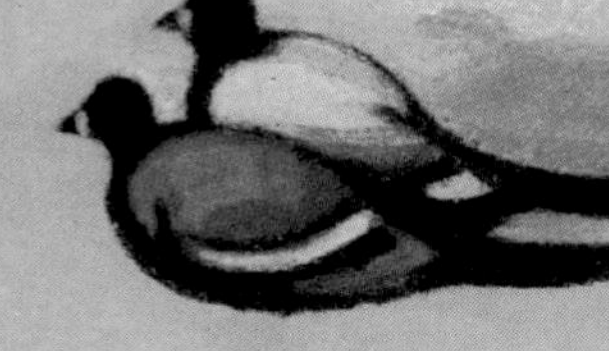

Lyle, Lyle, Crocodile *by Bernard Waber*

Lyle is a sweet, lovable crocodile. Why would anyone want him locked behind bars in a zoo?

Nine-in-One Grr! Grr! *told by Blia Xiong*

Tiger wants many tiger cubs in her family. But Black Bird hates tigers because they eat birds, so he plots to keep Tiger's family from growing.

The True Story of the Three Little Pigs *by Jon Scieszka*

The last time anyone saw the big bad wolf, he huffed and puffed his way into the little pigs' pot. Now Alexander T. Wolf (his real name) gets to tell his side of the story.

The Boy and the Ghost *by Robert D. San Souci*

A stranger leads Thomas to an old house with a treasure hidden inside. But there's a problem. The treasure is guarded by a fearsome ghost.

The Vingananee and the Tree Toad: A Liberian Tale *by Verna Aardema*

Spider and his animal friends enjoy their farm life until the terrible Vingananee comes and eats their stew.

Wolves

Thinking Focus

How are real wolves different from the wolves in storybooks?

Key Terms

predators
packs
den
communicate
extinct

In storybooks, wolves often sneak around dressed like grandmothers in order to trick and eat children. Or they might huff and puff, trying to catch three little pigs. In storybooks, you only see the "big bad wolf." But real wolves are very different from wolves in storybooks.

Real wolves are related to dogs, foxes, and jackals. They are **predators,** which means they hunt other wild animals for food. The most common wolf in North America is the gray wolf. Gray wolves usually have gray fur and can be as tall as three feet and weigh one hundred pounds.

In this lesson you will read about how real wolves — not storybook wolves — live in the wild.

How Wolves Live

In storybooks, wolves are almost always shown living alone and acting alone. In real life, wolves live in family groups called **packs.** Most packs have six or seven members. The leader of the pack is usually a male wolf. But there is also a female leader of the female wolves. The wolves in the pack follow the leaders.

Every adult member of the pack has a rank from highest to lowest. After a hunt, wolves eat in the order of their rank. When two wolves from the same pack want the same piece of meat, the wolf with the higher rank gets it.

An Arctic wolf pack.

Stop and Think

1. What is a wolf pack?
2. What happens when two wolves want the same thing?

How Wolves Care for Pups

In storybooks, wolves are almost never shown with their young. In real life, wolves spend a good deal of their time caring for the pups. Usually only the head male and female have pups. Before the pups are born, the female leader chooses a home for them. It is called a **den.** The den can be a big hole in the ground or it can be under a rock or in a log. In the den, the female wolf gives birth to about five or six pups. For about a month, the pups stay in the den and drink their mother's milk until they are old enough to eat solid food. Meanwhile, the other members of the pack bring meat for the mother wolf to eat. Finally the pups leave the den. The other wolves greet them by licking and smelling them, and wagging their tails. From then on, all the adult wolves take turns bringing food for the pups.

Gray wolf pups.

Stop and Think

1. What is a den?
2. How do the adult wolves of the pack help care for the pups?

How Wolves Communicate

In storybooks, wolves often talk just as people do. Real wolves can't talk. But they do have ways to **communicate** with other wolves. To communicate means to make something known to another. A high-ranking wolf lets the other wolves know that it is the leader by holding its head, ears, and tail high in the air. A low-ranking wolf shows respect for a high-ranking wolf by lowering its body and tail and flattening its ears. It will also lick the nose of the high-ranking wolf as a sign of respect.

Another way that wolves communicate is through sound. Pups will whimper to let other wolves know they are hungry. If a wolf gets lost, it will howl until its pack howls back. The lost wolf finds its way back to the pack by following the sound of the pack's howls. Wolf packs also howl to warn other wolf packs not to come closer.

A low-ranking wolf shows respect for a high-ranking wolf.

Stop and Think

1. How do wolves use sound to communicate?
2. How does a low-ranking wolf show respect to a high-ranking wolf?

Why Wolves Are in Danger

In storybooks, wolves are dangerous to people. In real life, people are dangerous to wolves. Years ago, wolves lived all over the world. Now wolves can be found in just a few places. Wolves are in danger of becoming **extinct.** If an animal becomes extinct, it means there are no more of that animal.

Territory occupied by wolves in North America.

In 1700's
Today

There are two reasons why wolves are disappearing. First, people have moved into the wild places where wolves like to live. When people settle into wild places and build buildings and roads, they push out wild animals. Wolves cannot find the food to hunt and eat. If wolves cannot find another place to live, they die.

Second, for many years people killed wolves. Hunters killed them for their beautiful fur. Farmers and ranchers killed wolves to keep them from eating their farm animals. But wolves only eat farm animals when they cannot find wild animals to hunt. Some people even killed wolves because they were afraid of them. But wolves usually avoid people and rarely attack them.

Stop and Think

1. What does it mean to say that an animal has become extinct?
2. What are two reasons why wolves are in danger of becoming extinct?

How Wolves Are Important in Nature

In storybooks, wolves eat other animals because they are evil or greedy. In real life, wolves help keep nature in balance. By eating other animals, wolves help keep the other animals' populations in control. For example, both wolves and moose live in Isle Royale National Park, an island in Lake Superior. If there were no wolves to eat the moose, there would be too many moose. The moose would get sick or die because there would not be enough food for all of them. Wolves do not eat so many moose that there are none left. Usually wolves can only catch sick, old, or very young moose. The healthy adult moose are left to have healthy babies.

A bull moose.

Stop and Think

1. What would happen to the moose on Isle Royale if there were no wolves?
2. How do wolves help to keep the moose herd on Isle Royale healthy?

Timber wolves eating a mule deer.

Saving Wolves from Extinction

Scientists are trying to save animals from becoming extinct. There once were hundreds of thousands of red wolves in the United States. A few years ago the red wolf, a cousin of the gray wolf, was almost extinct. There were none left in the wild. Only eighty red wolves were alive in the world and they all lived in zoos.

Then scientists set aside land for wolves. Laws were made to protect the wolves from being killed. Several red wolves were let go on the land. The wolves did very well in the wild and even had pups of their own.

Today the red wolf lives in wilderness areas of North Carolina and Tennessee.

Read books about nature and visit your local zoo to find out more about extinction and how you can help prevent it.

A red wolf.

Important Ideas

- Wolves live in family groups called packs, in which every member has a rank.
- There is a male leader and a female leader of the pack.
- Wolves communicate by using their bodies and by making sounds.
- Wolves are in danger of becoming extinct because people have killed large numbers of wolves.
- Wolves help to keep nature in balance by keeping other animals' populations down.

An Alaskan gray wolf.

Review

1. How are real wolves different from storybook wolves?
2. Why are wolves in danger of becoming extinct?
3. What are two things people can do to protect wolves and other animals from becoming extinct?

Write a Report

Write some questions about wolves that you might like answered. Then prepare a report on wolves by going to a library and reading books and magazine articles about wolves. Write two or three paragraphs that answer a question about wolves.

These questions might help you get started:

- How do wolf packs hunt for food?
- What are the different kinds of wolves? How are they alike and how are they different?

Glossary

Some of the words in this book may have pronunciations or meanings you do not know. This glossary can help you by telling you how to pronounce those words and by telling you the meanings with which those words are used in this book.

You can find out the correct pronunciation of any glossary word by using the special spelling after the word and the pronunciation key that runs across the bottom of the glossary pages.

The full pronunciation key opposite shows how to pronounce each consonant and vowel in a special spelling. The pronunciation key at the bottom of the glossary pages is a shortened form of the full key.

FULL PRONUNCIATION KEY

Consonant Sounds

b	**bib**	k	**c**at, **k**i**ck**, pi**que**	th	pa**th**, **th**in
ch	**ch**ur**ch**	l	**l**id, need**le**	*th*	ba**th**e, **th**is
d	**d**ee**d**	m	a**m**, **m**an, **m**u**m**	v	ca**v**e, val**v**e,
f	**f**ast, **f**i**f**e, o**ff**,	n	**n**o, sudde**n**		**v**ine
	phase, rou**gh**	ng	thi**ng**	w	**w**ith
g	**g**a**g**	p	**p**o**p**	y	**y**es
h	**h**at	r	**r**oa**r**	z	ro**s**e, si**z**e,
hw	**wh**ich	s	mi**ss**, **s**au**c**e, **s**ee		**x**ylophone,
j	**j**u**dg**e	sh	di**sh**, **sh**ip		**z**ebra
		t	**t**igh**t**	zh	gara**g**e,
					plea**s**ure, vi**s**ion

Vowel Sounds

ă	p**a**t	î	d**ea**r, d**ee**r,	ou	c**ow**, **ou**t
ā	**ai**d, th**ey**, p**ay**		f**ie**rce, m**e**re	ŭ	c**u**t, r**ou**gh
â	**ai**r, c**a**re, w**ea**r	ŏ	p**o**t, h**o**rrible	û	f**i**rm, h**ea**rd,
ä	f**a**ther	ō	g**o**, r**ow**, t**oe**		t**e**rm, t**u**rn,
ĕ	p**e**t, pl**ea**sure	ô	**a**lter, c**au**ght,		w**o**rd
ē	b**e**, b**ee**, **ea**s**y**,		f**o**r, p**aw**	yo͞o	ab**u**se, **u**se
	s**ei**ze	oi	b**oy**, n**oi**se, **oi**l	ə	**a**bout, sil**e**nt,
ĭ	p**i**t	o͝o	b**oo**k		penc**i**l, lem**o**n,
ī	b**y**, g**uy**, p**ie**	o͞o	b**oo**t		circ**u**s
				ər	butt**er**

STRESS MARKS

Primary Stress ′	*Secondary Stress* ′
bi•ol•o•gy [bī **ŏl**′ə jē]	bi•o•log•i•cal [bī′ə **lŏj**′ĭ kəl]

A

ab•ra•ca•dab•ra (ăb´ rə kə **dăb´** rə) A word once thought to have magical powers: *Waving a wand over the hat, the magician cried, "**Abracadabra!**"*

ab•so•lute•ly (ăb´ sə **lo͞ot´** lē) In truth; without a doubt. "Absolutely no dogs allowed in this garden" means that no dogs may enter the garden for any reason.

ad•mire (ăd **mīr´**) To look at and think about with pleasure or respect: *Of all the people Tom **admires,** the person he most looks up to is Martin Luther King, Jr.*

ap•pli•ca•tion (ăp´ lĭ **kā´** shən) The giving of medicine, especially by prescription: *The patient needed only one **application** of medicine to feel better.*

ar•roy•o (ə **roi´** ō) A deep ditch carved by flooding water. Arroyos are found in places where there is little rainfall, and the rain that does fall in such places causes floods.

art•ist (**är´** tĭst) A person who creates art: *The **artist** painted a picture of my house.*

as•sis•tant (ə **sĭs´** tənt) A person who helps out; a helper: *The doctor's **assistant** helped the doctor by answering the phone.*

awe•some (**ô´** səm) Causing feelings of wonder, amazement, and fear: *The astronaut's view of Earth from the Moon was an **awesome** sight.*

awl (ôl) A pointed tool for making holes in wood or leather: *The man used an **awl** to make holes in the belt.*

back•ing (băk′ ĭng) A large sheet of cloth to which the patches of a quilt are sewn.

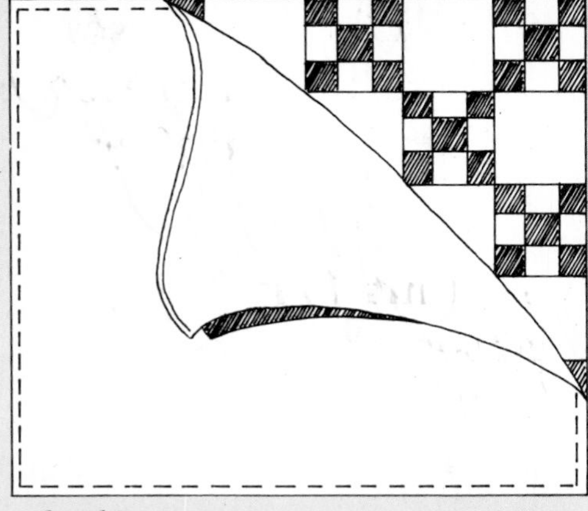
backing

bal•ance (băl′ əns) To make something steady so that it does not fall: *Can you* ***balance*** *that card so it stands on its edge without tipping over?*

bi•cus•pid (bī kŭs′ pĭd) A tooth with two points. An adult has eight bicuspids.

bind•ing (bīn′ dĭng) The long cloth strip that holds the pages of a book together.

board•ing school (bôr′ dĭng sko͞ol) A school at which students live during the school year: *When Sue went to* ***boarding school,*** *she lived in a room right across from the school library.*

book spine (bo͝ok spīn) The part of the book cover that joins the front and back covers.

book spine

o͞o **boot** / ou **out** / ŭ **cut** / û **fur** / *th* **the** / th **thin** / hw **which** / zh vision /
ə **a**go, it**e**m, penc**i**l, at**o**m, circ**u**s

brat•ty (brăt′ tē) Not well-behaved: *The **bratty** children acted badly when they didn't get what they wanted.*

cap•ture (**kăp′** chər) To catch and hold by force: *Alan was worried that Fritz had been **captured** by the enemy.*

cel•e•brate (**sĕl′** ə brāt′) To honor by acting in a special way: *They had a party to **celebrate** her birthday.*

CELEBRATE

Hundreds of years ago, *celebrate* came from a word that meant "famous."

cel•e•bra•tion (sĕl′ ə **brā′** shən) A party or activity in honor of a special occasion: *There was a big **celebration** for the new bride and groom after their wedding.*

cer•e•mo•ny (sĕr′ ə mō′ nē) A formal act or event performed in honor of a special occasion: *The children could be in the religious **ceremony** after they turned twelve.*

chal•lenge (chăl′ ənj) **1.** To demand that a person prove his or her ability: *Many people **challenged** Houdini to prove he really could escape.* **2.** A task that is difficult or takes a lot of effort: *It was a **challenge** to make jam out of all the plums because there were so many of them.*

chop•sticks (chŏp′stĭks′) A pair of thin sticks used for eating, especially in Asian countries.

chopsticks

ă pat / ā pay / â care / ä father / ĕ pet / ē be / ĭ pit / ī pie / î fierce / ŏ pot / ō go / ô paw, for / oi oil / ŏŏ book /

com•mand (kə **mănd´**) To direct; give orders to: *The magician **commanded** the man to crow like a rooster, and he did.*

con•stel•la•tion (kŏn´ stə **lā´** shən) A group of stars that is thought to look like an animal, a person, or an object and is named after it: *The Big Dipper is a **constellation** that looks like a spoon with a long handle.*

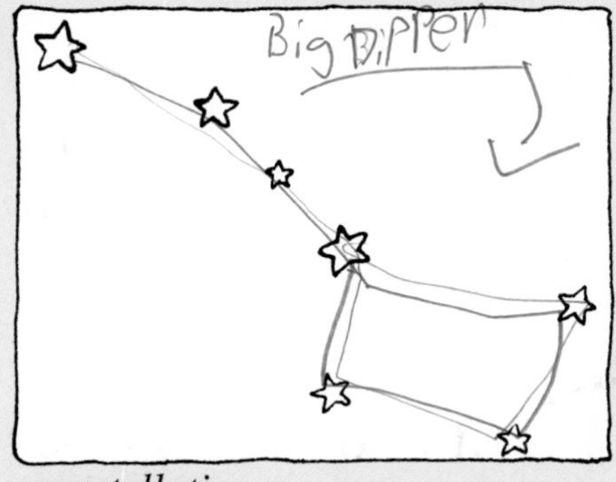

constellation

con•vinced (kən **vĭnsd´**) Caused to do or to believe something; made certain: *Anne was **convinced** something had happened to her dog, Tippy, when he didn't answer to her call.*

cun•ning (**kŭn´** ĭng) Clever in being able to trick or fool others: *The **cunning** little boy made the bully leave him alone by pretending to be sick.*

D

deaf ed•u•ca•tion (dĕf ĕj´ ə **kā´** shən) Instruction or classes for people who have hearing problems.

dec•o•rate (**dĕk´** ə rāt´) To make something more beautiful: *We will **decorate** the kitchen with flowers.*

de•vot•ed (dĭ **vō´** tĭd) Giving complete attention to one activity: *Pedro was so **devoted** to his tuba that he didn't have time for anything else.*

dis•guised (dĭs **gīzd´**) Changed in the way someone looks: *The witch was **disguised** as an old lady to trick Hansel and Gretel.*

---

o͞o **boot** / ou **out** / ŭ **cut** / û **fur** / *th* **the** / th **thin** / hw **which** / zh **vision** /
ə **ago, item, pencil, atom, circus**

dream (drēm) **1.** To think or believe that something is possible: *I hoped and **dreamed** I would win the contest.* **2.** A series of pictures or thoughts that people have during sleep: *My **dream** was about walking in a sunny field of flowers.*

eld•er (ĕl´ dər) A person who is older than most of the others in a group. Often the elders are thought to be the wisest of the group.

es•cape (ĭ **skāp´**) The act of getting free or breaking loose: *To **escape,** Houdini freed himself from the ropes tied around his wrists.*

fab•ric (**făb´** rĭk) Cloth.

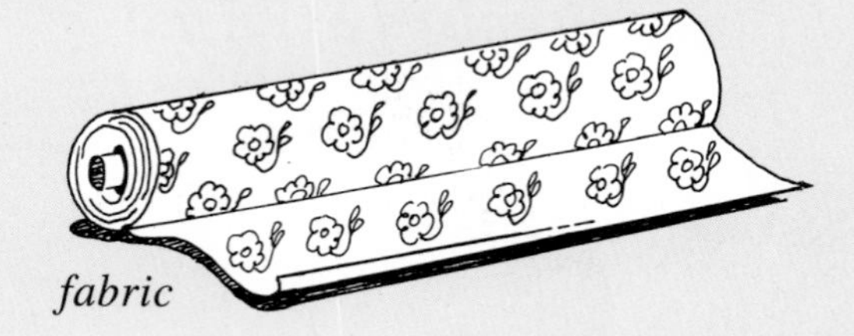

fabric

float•ing (**flō´** tĭng) Moving or resting in space without any support: *The princess was called the **floating** princess because she seemed to move through the air without having anything to hold her up.*

fu•ri•ous (**fyŏŏr´** ē əs) Very angry: *They were **furious** when they heard about the robbery.*

fu•ture (**fyōō´** chər) The time that is to come: *I talked about my **future** as a singer.*

gas (găs) A substance that is neither solid nor liquid: *There is a special **gas** that makes hot-air balloons rise.*

gauze (gôz) A very thin, loosely connected cloth that is often used to cover a wound.

goof it up (go͞of ĭt ŭp) Spoil or ruin something by making careless mistakes. When the children said Becky was goofing it up, they meant she was ruining the game.

heal•er (**hēl**´ ər) A person who uses folk medicine to cure illness: *The **healer** made some special tea to help get rid of my mother's headache.*

hear•ing im•paired (**hîr**´ ĭng ĭm **pârd**´) Unable to hear well. A program for the hearing impaired helps people who have trouble hearing or who are deaf.

hemp (hĕmp) A tall plant with tough stems that is used for making rope: *When stems of **hemp** are dried, they can be twisted into rope.*

hyp•no•tize (**hĭp**´ nə tīz´) To put someone into a relaxed but alert kind of sleep: *The magician **hypnotized** someone from the audience by making that person relax.*

il•lus•tra•tion (ĭl´ ə **strā**´ shən) A picture, diagram, or chart used to explain or decorate: *The **illustration** showed how to do the magic trick.*

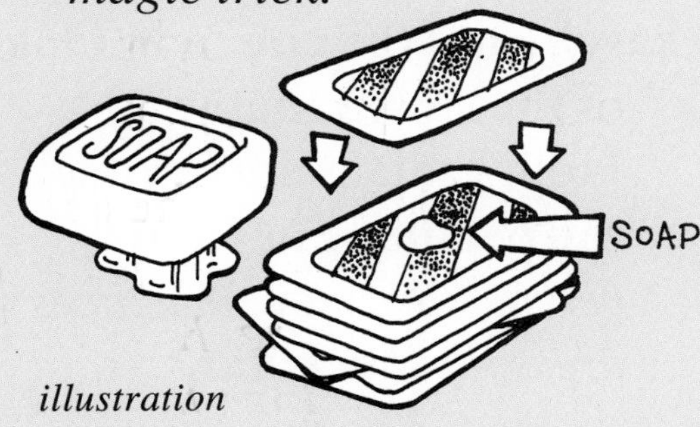

illustration

in•cense (**ĭn**´ sĕns´) A block or stick of perfume that gives off a pleasant smell when it is burned: *We burned **incense** to get rid of the smell of the skunk.*

INCENSE

The word *incense* once meant "to set on fire."

o͞o **boot** / ou **out** / ŭ **cut** / û **fur** / *th* **the** / th **thin** / hw **which** / zh **vision** / ə **ago, item, pencil, atom, circus**

in•spire (ĭn **spīr´**) To cause someone to think or act in a particular way: *My mother **inspired** me to learn to sew.*

ki•va (**kē´** və) An underground or partly underground Pueblo Indian building used for ceremonies.

jour•ney (**jûr´** nē) A trip: *For vacation, we are going to make a **journey** to Grandmother's.*

ka•chi•na (kə **chē´** nə) One of the spirits that visit Hopi Indians and protect the people: *For Hopi ceremonies, men sometimes dress like **kachinas**.*

kachina doll

lan•tern (**lăn´** tərn) A covering for a light that protects the light from air so that it will not go out: *When it got dark, we lit an old **lantern** so that we could set up our tent.*

latch (lăch) To close and lock with a bar: *Make sure to **latch** the pen so that the pigs don't get out.*

mar•vel (**mär´** vəl) Someone or something that causes surprise, astonishment, or wonder: *The crowd blinked with amazement at the **marvel** of the disappearing elephant.*

ă pat / ā pay / â care / ä father / ĕ pet / ē be / ĭ pit / ī pie / î fierce / ŏ pot / ō go / ô paw, for / oi oil / o͝o book /

mas•ter•piece (**măs**´ tər pēs´) An artist's greatest work. When Grandma said she was going to make a masterpiece, she meant that she was going to make the best quilt of her life.

MASTERPIECE

In the past, craftspeople presented their best work to a group of judges. If their work was good enough they would be called masters.

ma•te•ri•al (mə **tîr**´ ē əl) Cloth: *The quilt was sewn from many different kinds of* ***material.***

med•dle (**mĕd**´ l) To bother with other people's things or with their business: *Don't* ***meddle*** *with her drawing.*

mem•o•ry (**mĕm**´ ə rē) Something that is remembered: *I have happy* ***memories*** *of my third birthday.*

mid-air also **mid•air** (mĭd´ **âr**´) A point or region in the middle of the air: *When the balloon rose halfway to the ceiling, it was floating in* ***mid-air.***

mir•a•cle (**mĭr**´ ə kəl) An event that seems impossible because it cannot be explained: *Some magic tricks seem like* ***miracles*** *because people do not know how they are done.*

par•boil (**pär**´ boil´) To boil food for a short time: *She will* ***parboil*** *the corn and then freeze it.*

patch•work (**păch**´ wûrk´) Pieces of cloth of many different colors, shapes, and sizes sewn together.

pa•tient (**pā**´ shənt) A person who is treated by a doctor: *I am a* ***patient*** *of the new doctor who just moved to town.*

o͞o **boot** / ou **out** / ŭ **cut** / û **fur** / *th* **the** / th **thin** / hw **wh**ich / zh vision / ə **ago, item, pencil, atom, circus**

pat•tern (păt′ ərn) A special design that is repeated over and over: *The pieces of cloth were arranged in a special **pattern** of stars and stripes.*

per•form (pər **fôrm′**) To present before a group of people: *Our class **performed** a play for the whole school.*

per•me•ate (**pûr′** mē āt′) To pass through and spread throughout: *The medicine had to **permeate** the whole tooth to work.*

pi•ña•ta (pēn **yä′** tə) A decorated container filled with candy and small toys. The piñata is hung from the ceiling by a wire. Blindfolded children strike the piñata with sticks to break it open so that the candy and toys will fall out.

plum (plŭm) A small fruit with red, purple, or yellow skin.

plump (plŭmp) Rounded and full in shape: *Pick the peaches that are **plump** and juicy.*

poof (po͞of) A word used to show that something has disappeared: *Suddenly — **poof!** — the penny was gone.*

pos•i•tive•ly (**pŏz′** ĭ tĭv lē) Having no doubts. "Positively no dogs allowed in the garden" means no dogs may enter the garden at all.

pres•to (**prĕs′** tō) A word magicians use for sudden surprise: *The magician said **"Presto!"** and a rabbit jumped out of the hat.*

pro•ces•sion (prə **sĕsh′** ən) A group of people moving in an orderly forward direction: *On July 4, we will march in a **procession** across town.*

ă pat / ā pay / â care / ä father / ĕ pet / ē be / ĭ pit / ī pie / î fierce / ŏ pot / ō go / ô paw, for / oi oil / o͝o book /

pueb•lo (pwĕb´ lō) A village that is made up of buildings of stone and hardened mud. The buildings are built close together and on top of one another so that they look like one big building. Pueblos were built by Native Americans in the southwestern United States.

pueblo

PUEBLO

The word *pueblo* comes from an old word meaning "people." In a pueblo, many people live together in one place.

quilt (kwĭlt) A bed covering made by sewing together two layers of material with an inner layer of cotton, wool, down, or feathers.

quilt

QUILT

At one time, *quilt* meant "a sack filled with feathers." Today, some quilts are still filled with feathers.

rec•og•nize (rĕk´ əg nīz´) To know and remember from the past: *Even though I had not seen her since I was two, I* ***recognized*** *my aunt the moment I saw her.*

re•hearse (rĭ **hûrs´**) To practice in order to prepare for a performance: *To be sure he was ready for the show, Houdini* ***rehearsed*** *his magic tricks many times.*

re•lief (rĭ **lēf´**) A lessening of fear: *It was a* ***relief*** *to know that when Carmen slipped on the ice she was not hurt.*

re•tired (rĭ **tīrd´**) Gave up one's work, usually after reaching a certain age: *When the police officer said he was* ***retired,*** *he meant he no longer worked as a police officer.*

rev•er•ence (**rĕv´** ər əns) A feeling of respect mixed with love: *I remember my grandparents with* ***reverence.***

ripe (rīp) Fully grown: *Mr. Castle threw out the small, green plums and used only the large,* ***ripe*** *ones to make jam.*

risk (rĭsk) To take a chance.

rot•ten (**rŏt´** n) Very bad, decayed: *The tooth was so* ***rotten*** *it had to be pulled.*

sa•cred (**sā´** krĭd) Holy: *Nature is thought to be* ***sacred*** *by the Apaches, so they treat plants and animals with care.*

scene (sēn) A view; a place or event as seen by someone: *In the* ***scene*** *drawn by the girl, there were some children playing hopscotch.*

se•ri•ous•ly (**sîr´** ē əs lē) Not joking or fooling: *It's hard to take Sarah* ***seriously*** *because she is always acting silly.*

ser•pent (**sûr´** pənt) Snake.

shep•herd (**shĕp´** ərd) A person who takes care of a flock of sheep: *The* ***shepherd*** *was careful not to let his sheep get lost.*

ă pat / ā pay / â care / ä father / ĕ pet / ē be / ĭ pit / ī pie / î fierce / ŏ pot / ō go / ô paw, for / oi oil / o͝o book /

sign (sīn) **1.** To use a language made up of hand motions instead of speech: *Becky couldn't speak, so she **signed** to tell what she meant.* **2.** To write your name, usually on an official paper. **3.** A board or poster that tells information.

spell (spĕl) **1.** A word or group of words thought to have magic power: *When Abdul Gasazi cast a **spell** on Fritz, he changed the dog into a duck.* **2.** To name or write in the correct order the letters that form a word.

stitch (stĭch) One complete movement of a threaded needle into and out of material in sewing: *Mother used tiny **stitches** to sew the hem in my dress.*

stitch

stub•born (stŭb′ ərn) Refusing to change an idea or purpose even though others want you to change: *When the mayor said the stranger was **stubborn,** he meant that the stranger wouldn't change his mind.*

stunt (stŭnt) An act that shows unusual skill and bravery: *The rider performed many dangerous **stunts** such as jumping onto the back of a galloping horse.*

stunt

sug•gest (səg **jĕst′**) To offer for thought or action: *He **suggested** a good movie for the whole family to see.*

ōō **boot** / ou **out** / ŭ **cut** / û **fur** / *th* **the** / th **thin** / hw **which** / zh **vision** /
ə **ago, item, pencil, atom, circus**

ta•ma•le (tə **mä´** lē) Ground meat seasoned with chili, rolled in cornmeal dough, and then wrapped in cornhusks and steamed.

tex•ture (**tĕks´** chər) The feel of something: *No two patches of cloth had the same* ***texture****. Some felt soft; others felt rough.*

tor•ti•lla (tôr **tē´** yə) Flat, round bread made of flour or cornmeal. Tortillas are often filled with ground beef or vegetables.

tra•di•tion (trə **dĭsh´** ən) An idea or custom that is passed down over many years: *Having turkey for Thanksgiving dinner is a* ***tradition*** *in my family.*

TRADITION

Tradition once meant "to hand down."

treat (trēt) To try to cure; to give medical help: *The doctor tried to* ***treat*** *the patient's toothache.*

treat•ment (**trēt´** mənt) The use of something to cure a disease: *The doctor gave the boy some medicine as a* ***treatment*** *for his illness.*

van•ish (**văn´**ĭsh) To disappear; become invisible: *The elephant* ***vanished*** *and was never seen again.*

wast•ed (**wā´** stĭd) Spent or used foolishly: *Tina couldn't take a bubble bath because Peggy* ***wasted*** *all the bubble bath washing the dog.*

ă pat / ā pay / â care / ä father / ĕ pet / ē be / ĭ pit / ī pie / î fierce / ŏ pot / ō go / ô paw, for / oi oil / ŏŏ book / ōō boot / ou out / ŭ cut / û fur / *th* the / th thin / hw which / zh vision / ə ago, item, pencil, atom, circus

Acknowledgments

For each of the selections listed below, grateful acknowledgment is made for permission to excerpt and/or reprint original or copyrighted material, as follows:

Major Selections

And It Is Still That Way: Legends Told by Arizona Indian Children With Notes by Byrd Baylor, copyright © 1976 by Byrd Baylor. Reprinted by permission of Trails West Publishing, Santa Fe, New Mexico.

Becky, by Karen Hirsch, Copyright © 1981 by Carolrhoda Books, Inc. 241 First Avenue North, Minneapolis, MN 55401. Reprinted by permission of the publishers.

Doctor De Soto, by William Steig. Copyright © 1982 by William Steig. Reprinted by permission of Farrar, Straus and Giroux, Inc.

Family Pictures, by Carmen Lomas Garza. Published by Children's Book Press. Copyright © 1990 by Carmen Lomas Garza. Reprinted by permission of GRM Associates, Inc., Agents for Children's Book Press.

The Farolitos of Christmas, by Rudolfo A. Anaya, illustrated by Richard C. Sandoval. Copyright © 1987 by Rudolfo A. Anaya. *The Farolitos of Christmas* is distributed in book form by the University of New Mexico Press, Albuquerque, NM 87131, and by New Mexico Magazine, Santa Fe, NM 87503. Reprinted by permission of Rudolfo A. Anaya and Richard C. Sandoval.

"The Floating Princess," from *Magicians Do Amazing Things*, by Robert Kraske. Copyright © 1979 by Robert Kraske. Reprinted by permission of Random House, Inc.

The Garden of Abdul Gasazi, by Chris Van Allsburg. Copyright © 1979 by Chris Van Allsburg. Reprinted by permission of Houghton Mifflin Company.

"The Great Houdini," from the book by Anne Edwards. Text copyright © 1977 by Anne Edwards. Reprinted by permission of G. P. Putnam's Sons, and A. P. Watt Ltd.

Jam: A True Story, by Margaret Mahy, illustrated by Helen Craig. Text copyright © 1985 by Margaret Mahy. Illustrations copyright © 1985 by Helen Craig. Reprinted by permission of Little, Brown and Company, and J. M. Dent & Sons.

Lon Po Po: A Red-Riding Hood Story from China, translated and illustrated by Ed Young, copyright © 1989 by Ed Young. Reprinted by permission of Philomel Books, a division of The Putnam & Grosset Group, and McIntosh and Otis.

The Patchwork Quilt, by Valerie Flournoy, pictures by Jerry Pinkney. Text copyright © 1985 by Valerie Flournoy. Pictures copyright © 1985 by Jerry Pinkney. Reprinted by permission of the publisher, Dial Books for Young Readers.

"Six Magic Tricks You Can Do," from *Now You See It: Easy Magic for Beginners*, by Ray Broekel and Laurence B. White, Jr. Text copyright © 1979 by Laurence B. White, Jr. and Ray Broekel. Reprinted by permission of Little, Brown and Company.

Poetry

"Alligator," from *Come On Into My Tropical Garden: Poems for Children*, by Grace Nichols, illustrated by Caroline Binch. Text copyright © 1988 by Grace Nichols; illustration copyright © 1988 by Caroline Binch. Reprinted by permission of A & C Black (Publishers) Ltd.

"Andre," from *Bronzeville Boys and Girls*, by Gwendolyn Brooks. Copyright © 1956 by Gwendolyn Brooks Blakely. Reprinted by permission of HarperCollins Publishers Inc.

"Everybody Says," from *Everything and Anything*, by Dorothy Aldis. Copyright 1925, 1926, 1927, copyright renewed 1953, 1954, 1955 by Dorothy Aldis. Reprinted by permission of G. P. Putnam's Sons.

"Grasshopper Gumbo," from *The New Kid on the Block*, by Jack Prelutsky. Copyright © 1984 by Jack Prelutsky. Reprinted by permission of William Morrow and Company, Inc./Publishers, New York.

"I Am a Ghost Who's Lost His Boo," from *The New Kid on the Block*, by Jack Prelutsky. Copyright © 1984 by Jack Prelutsky. Reprinted by permission of William Morrow and Company, Inc./Publishers, New York.

"I'm in a Rotten Mood," from *The New Kid on the Block*, by Jack Prelutsky. Copyright © 1984 by Jack Prelutsky. Reprinted by permission of William Morrow and Company, Inc./Publishers, New York.

"Mother's Day," by Takeuchi Yumiko, from *There Are Two Lives: Poems by Children of Japan*, edited by Richard Lewis and translated by Haruna Kimura. Copyright © 1964 by Akane Book Company, Tokyo. Reprinted by permission of the Japanese Government Agency for Cultural Affairs.

"The New Kid on the Block," from *The New Kid on the Block*, by Jack Prelutsky. Copyright © 1984 by Jack Prelutsky. Reprinted by permission of William Morrow and Company, Inc./Publishers, New York.

"A Warning About Bears," "More About Bears," "Still More About Bears," "Last Word About Bears," by John Ciardi, from *You Read to Me, I'll Read to You*. Illustration by Edward Gorey. Copyright © 1962 by John Ciardi. Reprinted by permission of Harper & Row, Publishers, Inc.

Quotations from Authors/Illustrators

Margaret Mahy (pg. 52), from Authorgraph No. 24: "Margaret Mahy," in *Books for Keeps*, No. 24, January, 1984, pp. 12–13. Copyright © 1984 by the School Bookshop Association Ltd. Reprinted by permission of the School Bookshop Association Ltd.

Additional Acknowledgments

"Before You Turn the Page" (pg. 85), adapted from *110 Great Magic Tricks.* Copyright © 1978, S. S. Adams Company, Neptune, NJ 07754-0850.

Credits

Program Design Carbone Smolan Associates

Cover Design Carbone Smolan Associates

Design **8–23, 34–53** DeFrancis Studio; **24–33** Waters Design Associates, Inc.; **56–97** WGBH; **98–101** Sibley/Peteet Design; **102–193** Louise Fili Ltd.; **194–251** Sheaff Design, Inc.; **252–259** Pronk & Associates

Introduction (left to right) 1st row: Superstock; James L. Ballard; Fred Lynch; 2nd row: Mike Schroeder; Leslie Holt Morrill; Renée Graef; 3rd row: James L. Ballard; Brian Lies; Robert Copeland/Westlight; 4th row: Renée Graef; DeFrancis Studio; Nancy Sheehan

Table of Contents **4** David Henderson/Eric Roth Studio; **5** Brian Lies; **6** Teofilo Olivieri

Illustration **12–22** Helen Craig; **24–33** Renée Graef; **36–50** Jerry Pinkney; **51** DeFrancis Studio; **57–59** Brian Lies; **60–76** Leslie Holt Morrill; **77** Brian Lies; **78–83** Kevin Hawkes; **85, 87–93, 96–97** Brian Lies; **98–101** Mike Schroeder; **103–105** Teofilo Olivieri; **106–135** Carmen Lomas Garza; **136** Teofilo Olivieri; **137** Carmen Lomas Garza; **139–164** Richard C. Sandoval; **165** Teofilo Olivieri; **169–190** from the book *And It Is Still That Way* by Byrd Baylor; **191–193** Teofilo Olivieri; **198–208** William Steig; **210–223** Ed Young; **224–240** Chris Van Allsburg; **242–243** Edward Gorey; **244–245** Caroline Binch; **247** William Steig; **248** Ed Young; **249** Chris Van Allsburg; **250–251** Fred Lynch; **263, 266** Sharron Holm/Cornell & McCarthy; **265** Meg Kelleher-Aubrey; **267, 273** Susan Banta

Photography **10** Myrleen Ferguson/Photo Edit (upper left); **10** Tony Freeman/Photo Edit (top center); **10** Lawrence Migdale (bottom left); **10** Lawrence Migdale (bottom center); **11** Brent Jones (upper left); **11** Myrleen Ferguson/Photo Edit (center right); **11** Kathy Tarantola/The Picture Cube (bottom left); **11** Lawrence Migdale (bottom center); **11** Myrleen Ferguson/Photo Edit (bottom center); **11** Superstock (lower right); **34** Jim Whitmer; **35** Suzanne Murphy/FPG International (top right); **35** Superstock (top left); **35** Jim Whitmer (center); **35** David Young Wolff/Photo Edit (bottom); **52** Courtesy of Margaret Mahy (top right); **52** Courtesy of Karen Hirsch (top center); **52** Valerie Flournoy (top right); **52** Margaret Mahy, Photo: Foster/Icon (bottom); **53** Courtesy of Karen Hirsch (top); **53** Courtesy of E. P. Dutton (bottom); **94** Courtesy of Anne Edwards (top); **94** Courtesy of Robert Kraske (bottom); **95** Courtesy of Ray Broekel (left); **95** Courtesy of Laurence B. White (right); **98** Photograph © 1991 by Jill Krementz; **138** Rudolfo Anaya; **166** Jim Ambrose/Macmillan; **167** Joe Herrera (Cochiti) "Petroglyph Figures" c.1952–56, casein on paper, 23" x 57", Courtesy of The Heard Museum, Phoenix, AZ; **168** Julian Martinez (San Ildefonso) b.1897–d.1943 "Pottery Design," n.d. watercolor paper, 52 x 65 cm, Courtesy of The Heard Museum, Phoenix, AZ; **172** Michael Kabotie (Hopi) b.1942 "Petroglyphs," 1967, casein on paper, 38.1 x 50.8 cm, Courtesy of The Heard Museum, Phoenix, AZ; **176** "Recurrence of Spiritual Elements," acrylic painting by Helen Hardin. © Helen Hardin 1973. Photo credit © Cradoc Bagshaw 1991, Courtesy of The Heard Museum, Phoenix, AZ; **179** Pop Chalee/ Merina Lujan Hopkins (Taos) b.1906 "Enchanted Forest," n.d. watercolor on paper, 48.5 x 63.8 cm, Courtesy of The Heard Museum, Phoenix, AZ; **183** Fred Beaver (Creek) b.1911–d.1980 "The Orator," 1973, tempera on paper, 45.5 x 61 cm, Courtesy of The Heard Museum, Phoenix, AZ; **186** Ha So De/Narciso P. Abeyta (Navajo) b. 1918 "Changeable Wolf Man," 1958, casein on paper, 77 x 56 cm, Courtesy of The Heard Museum, Phoenix, AZ; **195** Bill Ross/West Light; **196** Robert Copeland/West Light; **209** Superstock (center left); **209** Brian Parker/Tom Stack and Associates (center right); **209** Superstock (top left); **209** Superstock (top right); **209** Superstock (bottom left); **209** Michael Melford/The Image Bank (bottom right); **225** Richard Megna/Fundamental Photo; **241** Richard Megna/ Fundamental Photo; **246** Nancy Crampton (left); **246** Sean Kernan/The Putnam and Grosset Group (center); **246** Kristin Craig (right); **252** David Hiser/The Image Bank; **253** Comstock; **254** Animals Animals/© Charles Palek; **255** Animals Animals/© Charles Palek (bottom right); **255** William Munoz (top right); **257** John Warden (top); **257** Animals Animals/© Stouffer Productions (bottom); **258** Animals Animals/© Jim Tuten; **259** Masterfile; **263** Gabor Demjen/Aperture; **264** Dion Ogust/The Image Works; **268** John Running; **271** Bill Aron/Photo Edit; **271** Peter Menzel/Stock Boston (left); **Assignment Photographers** David Henderson/Eric Roth Studio **10–11** (background), **34–35** (background), **52–53** (background), **54–55**. David Shopper **86–92**.